"Creangă managed to perfectly convey both the spatial and timely positioning of his account, as well as all the details of an ingenuous and restless universe."
—Writer Norman Manea

"Here, as in his stories and novellas, Creangă effects the passage from the popular level of literature to its cultured level, following a strictly spontaneous path by organically developing a talent exercised throughout the past of an old rural culture, now reaching a point where it surpasses itself."
—Critic Tudor Vianu

"Creangă did not invent stories: he had enough material already. The book is full of funny stories, presented in a hilarious way."
—A reader

# Recollections from Childhood

by
ION CREANGĂ

translated from Romanian by
LUCY BYNG

revised by
TIBERIAN PRESS

TIBERIAN PRESS

Recollections from Childhood
Original title in Romanian: *Amintiri din copilărie*

Published by Tiberian Press
PO Box 1662
Huntersville, NC 28070
www.tiberianpress.com

Printed in the United States of America.
First edition.
18 17 16 15 14 13 12 11 10 9 8 7 6 5 4

ISBN: 1-950827-09-7
ISBN-13: 978-1-950827-09-1

# CONTENTS

# PREFACE

HAD it not been for the foundation in Jassy of a literary society called *Junimea*, Ion Creangă would not have written a single word. Of course, he would have been known and admired as a storyteller by his own village folk of Humuleshti among whom he was born in 1837. But his coming into touch with the members of the *Junimea* society, especially with the critic Maiorescu and the poet Eminescu, made him conscious of his inborn talent and, encouraged by them, he set out to write of what he himself had known, independently of any outside influence.

His largest work, Recollections, covers a period prior to the union of the Romanian Provinces. Moldavia had its own more or less settled government, under which efforts were made to educate the peasants—efforts looked upon rather suspiciously by the latter. What was the use? Had they not lived for centuries without schooling? So thought the father of Ion Creangă; whilst his mother, wishing to see him a priest, argued: "For shame, man! You will go to the bottomless pit of hell and you will have no one to pull you out of it if you don't exert yourself to make your boy a priest."

About this period of his life Ion Creangă tells of many adventures, giving at the same time a true insight into Moldavian peasant life, with its joys and sorrows, its beliefs and age-long significant customs. Every line of his reflects the spirit of the people, illuminated both by humor and subdued pathos.

Naturally an author deeply rooted in the soil, with a pronounced idiomatic style savoring of peasant vigor and shrewdness, is far from easy to translate. Once, however, the difficulties surmounted by one like Mrs. Lucy Byng, who does her work for nothing else but the pure love of it, such an author becomes all the more interesting, as he brings forth to the general understanding a new and fresh side of literary expression.

Is not this a sufficient reason for presenting Ion Creangă to the kind attention of the British public?

Marcu Beza
London, 22nd May, 1930

# CHAPTER I

SOMETIMES I stop to think of the times and the people there were in our part of the world, when I, little dear, began to grow into a boy in my parents' house in the town of Humuleshti, right on the Neamtzu river; it was a large, cheerful town, divided into three parts, all touching each other, the Middle Town, and Deleni and Bejeni. For even then Humuleshti wasn't just a town without any important people; but an old-established town, settled in every sense of the word, with various well-to-do citizens, with sturdy youths, and handsome girls, who knew how to dance the hora, and how to wield their shuttles till the town vibrated with the sound of looms on every side; with a fine church, and various priests and students and parishioners who were an honor to their town. And Father Ioan at the bottom of the hill, Lord, what a worthy and kindly man that was! At his instigation what a lot of trees were planted in the cemetery, which was surrounded by a wooden fence with a roof of shingles, and what a room he built near the church door for a school, and then how indefatigably the priest walked about the town, from house to house, accompanied by Vasile Ilioai, a sturdy bachelor, handsome and stalwart, to advise people to send their children to school. A crowd of boys and girls assembled at the school; I was among them, an insignificant boy, blushing, and afraid of my own shadow.

The best scholar was the priest's own Esmeralda herself, a minx of a child, quite capable enough to surpass the boys altogether, not only at their books, but also at their pranks. The priest came nearly every day to the school to see what was going on. Then there came the day when the priest arrived and, brought us a new high chair, and after he had asked the master how we were behaving, he stood a moment in thought, and then he called the chair "The Bay Horse," and left it in the school.

Another day we were faced with the priest again at the school, and with him Mosh Fotea, the town furrier, who brought us a new school gift, a love of a little whip of thongs beautifully plaited, and the priest called it "Saint Nicholas," as that was the patron saint of Humuleshti church. Then he begged Mosh Fotea if he came across some good thongs to put them together from time to time, and to make another, thicker, whip if he could. Master Vasile smiled then, but we school children looked at each other with horror-stricken eyes. The priest made a rule, and said that every Saturday the boys and girls were to have repetition, that is to say, the master was to hear all that each one had learnt during the week, and each mistake was to be chalked up on

4

something, and finally for every fault the scholar would earn a "Saint Nicholas."

Then the priest's child, who was audacious and full of naughtiness, burst out laughing. Woe betide her, poor thing!

"You will mount the Bay Horse, if you please, young lady," said the priest, very sternly, "we will make you a present of Saint Nicholas, the one hanging on the nail on the wall."

In spite of the intervention of Mosh Fotea and Master Vasile he beat Esmeralda severely; afterwards she sat with her hands before her eyes, and wept like a bride, till her very chemise heaved with her sobs. When we saw this we were petrified. But the priest, bringing rolls and scones day after day, pacified us, and the work went on steadily; the boys' lessons varied each day, and on Saturday there was repetition.

It's true we sometimes did as we liked; from the alphabet-table, and letters written out by schoolmaster Vasile for each of us, we went on to copybooks, and from copybooks to the Book of Hours, and then, God help us! In the absence of the priest and the schoolmaster, we went into the cemetery, held the Book of Hours open, and as its pages were rather greasy they attracted the gnats and flies, and when we banged-to the book we annihilated some ten or twenty souls at one time; it was all up with the gnats! One day the priest came and found the Book of Hours, and when he saw the bloody state it was in he clasped his head with despair. But when he learned the reason he began to invite each of us to mount the Bay Horse, and to comfort us with the blessed Hierarch Nicholas on account of the suffering of the pious gnats, and of the pious flies, which had perished through our fault.

Not long after this, and on a day in the month of May, about the time of the Great Fair, unfortunately the devil induced stupid Vasile, for I can call him nothing else, to set one Nică Costache to hear my repetition. Nică, a big boy who knew absolutely nothing, had quarreled with me on account of the priest's Esmeralda, to whom, to my great regret, I had one day given a cuff because she would not let me catch flies in peace. Well, Nică began to hear me, and he listened and he listened, and now he began to chalk up my mistakes wholesale on a slate, one, two, up to twenty-nine. "Eh! This is past a joke," said I to myself, "and he has not yet finished hearing me, and who knows how many there will be." And it began to grow black before my eyes, and I to shake with fury. "Well, well, now or never. What's to be done, Nică?" said I to myself. I looked furtively towards the door of deliverance, and I began to shuffle my feet as I waited impatiently for some idle scholar to come in from outside, for the order was that we should not be out two at a time; I gnashed my teeth when I saw that no one came to save me from riding the Bay Horse, and from the blessings of Nicholas, patron of bruises. But the real Saint Nicholas realized my situation, for just then a good-for-nothing boy came into the school. Then, in spite of everything, I made for the door, and rushed out; I did not linger in the school ground, but took to my heels for home. When I looked back two lanky youths were after me; and now I began to tear along, I passed our home but did not go into the house, I turned to the left, and entered a courtyard, and out of the courtyard into a farmyard, and out of the farmyard into the maize field, half of which had just been hoed, and after me came the boys. But before they got up to me I, urged by fear, had succeeded, I know not how, in hiding myself in the field at the base of a sheaf of maize. And Nică Costache, my enemy, and with him Toader, the other lanky youth, passed by me talking to each other with great annoyance, and it is plain God had blinded them that they might not find me. And after a time, hearing neither a rustling among the maize nor the scratching of a hen, I sprang up with straw on my head, and went off quick to my mother at home, where I began to tell her with tears that I would never go to school again even if they killed me. But the next day the priest visited us and came to an understanding with father; they treated me kindly, but took me again for school. "For it is a pity to be without a scrap of learning," said the priest; "you have already passed from the A.B.C. and the Spelling Book; you are at the Book of Hours now, and any day may pass on to the Psalter, which is the key to all knowledge, and who knows what time will bring; it may be you will become priest here at the church of St. Nicholas, for I shall exert myself on your behalf. I have an only daughter, and I shall have to see whom I shall choose for a son-in-law."

Well, well, when I heard talk of being priest, and of Father's Esmeralda, I left the flies alone and began to have other thoughts, other plans. I began to try to write, I swung the incense-burner in church, and intoned the responses. And the Father took me under his wing, and Esmeralda began from time to time to dazzle me with a glance, and Vasile set me to hear other boys, and the mill ground quite different grist now. The hoarse, clumsy and wicked Nică Costache no longer had the mastership over me. But man proposes and God disposes. One day, and actually on St. Foca's Day, the Sheriff took men from the town for forced labor to mend the roads. It was said the Prince would pass through on his way to the monastery. And Vasile, who had nothing better to do, let us too help on the road in order that the Prince when he passed should not say our town was lazier than any other town. So we left school, and all went together. And some dug with spades, and some wheeled wheelbarrows, some pushed carts, some carried hods, everyone worked with zeal. But the Sherriff and the Vice-Mayor and some dirty tax collectors walked up and down among the men; then suddenly we saw some men in a group by the side of the road, and one of them was groaning loudly.

"What's happening there?" asked men, coming up from all sides.

They caught friend Vasile for the army surreptitiously; they pinioned him firmly, put hand-cuffs on him, and sent him to Piatra. That is why the

Sherriff had the men out on forced labor. In those day they caught lads for the army by craft. It was a horrid sight! The other young men made themselves scarce, while we children went home crying. "Cursed be that dog of a Sherriff, and as he tortured a mother's heart, so may St. Foca from today on torture his heart, and the hearts of all his abettors,"...thus cursed the women all through the town with bitter tears. But Vasile's mother went to Piatra to the boy, lamenting him as though he were dead!

"Come, mother, the world is just what you make of it," said friend Vasile, to comfort her, "and a man can live well in the army if he is capable. St. George and St. Dimitrie, and other martyred saints were warriors, and perished for the love of Christ; if only we might be as they were!'"

Well, well, we lost friend Vasile, he went where it was ordained that he should go. And Father Ioan wandered about with his hair streaming in the wind, seeking for a schoolmaster, but he never found another Vasile, wise, industrious, and modest as a young girl. Schoolmaster Iordache was in the town, the nasal-voiced man in the principal pew, but what good was he? There is no doubt that he knew the church services by heart, but he shook with old age, and moreover he was addicted to the bottle. And so for a time the school was deserted, but some of us followed Father Ioan about; it was all to our good, for the Church opens man's mind. On Sunday we hummed in the pews, and stole a cake! And when the two fast days came, some thirteen or fourteen of us boys ran in front of the priest, sweeping away the snow from one house after the other, and at Christmas we neighed like foals, while at the Epiphany we sang the Kyrie Eleison till the town rang. And when the priest arrived we arranged ourselves in two rows, and opened up a path for him, while he held his beard and said proudly to his host:

"These are the priest's foals, my son. Important days like these they look forward to all the year with great pleasure. Have you prepared any boiled beans, sippets, rice tarts, or any cooked cabbage?"

"I have prepared, honored Father; have the goodness to bless our house and table, and please be seated that your petitioners may be seated too."

When we heard talk of a meal we hurled ourselves upon it, and then keep your mouth from watering if you can, as the saying goes:

"We laugh to see the tarts of rice,
At sight of cabbage we laugh twice."

What would you have; after all, the fasts only came twice a year. At one place I remember we scrambled so that we upset the man's table, and all the dishes on it, in the middle of the house, so that the Father's cheeks burned with shame. But he said, mildly:

"Where there is nothing you cannot upset anything, my sons, but a little care does no harm."

The feast of the patron Saint of our church lasted

a whole week, and one had not got a big enough stomach in which to stow away the coliva and meats, there were so many. Teachers, priests and prelates, and every kind of person from all over the place assembled at the patronal feast of Humuleshti, and they all went away satisfied. In private houses a crowd of guests were entertained, and my mother, God help her, would enjoy it greatly when guests met at our house, and she had the chance of breaking bread with them.

"Never mind, the boys may give alms for my soul after my death or they may not; it is better for me to give with my own hand. Whatever happens one thinks of oneself first. I shall have seen it done!"

While I was learning at school, my mother learned with me at home, and could read the Book of Hours, the Psalter, and the Life of Alexander of Macedonia better than I could, and she rejoiced greatly when she saw me eager to learn.

As for my father, who often said to me in joke:

"The learned man hangs the cheese on a nail,
Has sour milk in the ink-pot,
And trouble in his pocket."

He thought we had better remain like Nica Shtefan of Petri, an honest man, and a respected citizen in Humuleshti. As the proverb says:

"Better be first in the village than last in the town."

My mother was ready to wear herself out that I might go on learning. My mother tormented my father to send me somewhere to school, for she had heard it said at church: "The learned man will grow wise, and will have the ignorant for his servant."

Besides this, the old witch with her forty-one peas in the bottom of the sieve, all the stargazers and fortunetellers whom she visited on my account, and all the women belonging to the church in the village, put all sorts of queer ideas into my mother's head, each one stranger than the last; that I should be in the company of great men, that I had as much luck as a toad has hair, that I had the voice of an angel, and many other marvels, so that my mother, in her weakness for me, came to believe that I should arrive at being a second Cucuzel, the ornament of Christianity, who drew tears from every stony heart, carried the light to the people in the wilderness and enchanted the whole of humanity with his voice.

"Lord, woman, Lord, you want a deal more sense," said my father, seeing how ambitious she was for me. "If everyone is a scholar there will be no one to take our boots off. Have you never heard them tell how a fellow went to Paris an ox, and came back a cow? And where did Grigore Petre Lucă from our village get his learning from? Yet he knows enough to tell many jokes and say verses at wedding feasts. Don't you see that unless he has sense in his head there's no use in it at all?"

"That may be so or it may not," said my mother, "I

want to make the boy a priest, that's what I want."

"Priest at all cost," said my father. "Listen to that! Can't you see he is a useless boy, good-for-nothing, and lazy beyond compare? In the early morning he's a trouble to wake. Directly he gets up he wants food. While he's a little boy he catches flies in the Book of Hours, and all day he wanders along the river banks to try and get a bathe instead of looking after the weaned lambs and giving me all the help he's capable of. In the winter, he's on the ice and on the slide. You, with your schooling, got him into bad habits. When he gets bigger, he'll begin to run after the petticoats, and at that rate I shall never get any use out of him."

And as I have the honor to tell you, a good many words passed between my father and my mother on my account until there came that summer in August, the famous cholera epidemic of '48, which began to mow down in Humuleshti to right and left, so that on every side one heard nothing but sorrow and lamentation. And I, impatient as I always was, of course went out to the gate as they bore the dead past our door, and followed them to the church, and came home with my shirt full of cracknels, apples, gilded nuts, locust-beans, and figs from the offerings in memory of the dead, and my father and mother were beside themselves when they saw me with them. To avoid danger for me they sent me to the sheepfold in the Agapa forest close to Cără-Gitza bridge where our sheep were, and I was to remain there till the pestilence abated, but during the night

13

the cholera overtook me, and I was feverish and tore my hair, and I was scorched by thirst, but the shepherds and the man who made the cheeses took no heed of me; they turned over when I cried out, and snored again. Meanwhile I dragged myself as well as I could to the spring at the back of the fold, and in a moment I had drunk a whole bucketful of water; I may say that that night the spring was my resting place, and I did not close my eyes a second. Soon after day-break, our sheep-milker, Vasile Bordeianu, decided to go to Humuleshti, a journey of two hours on foot, and he persuaded my father to bring a carriage, and take me home. On the way I asked incessantly for water, but my father cleverly got me past fountain after fountain, until by the grace of God I reached Humuleshti. The village doctors, Mosh Vasile Tzandură and another one, I don't remember which, were at our house, and were by the fire melting some wax and grease in a big pan, and after they had given me a good rubbing with vinegar and lovage, they spread melted wax on a sheet, and swaddled me in it like a baby, and I don't know what happened afterwards but I fell dead asleep, and the next day, as the Angelus was ringing, I woke up cured, altogether cured; may God bless Mosh Tzandură and his companion. As a proverb says "A bad penny turns up again." By the evening, I had wandered over nearly the whole village; at the bathing-place I had actually run a race with my friend Chiriac Goian, a vagabond and idler like myself. But my father did not say anything to me, he let me go my own way for a bit.

During the winter my mother tried to persuade my father to send me to school somewhere. But my father said he had no more money for me.

"I used to give Schoolmaster Vasile Vasilică twenty kreutzers a month. But that scoundrel of a master, Simon Fosa at Tzutzuene, just because he can quote more than other people, and takes snuff all day, asks some sixty kreutzers a month, do you hear that? This boy, clothes and all, will never earn as much as I have already spent upon him."

When my mother heard this she was furious.

"You silly man, how can you even understand me when you can't even read? When you spend kreutzers on your mustache, why don't you complain? Hasn't Petre Todosuicăi, our publican, taken hundreds of lei off you, and hasn't Vasile Roibu of Bejeni taken more, and others too? Rushta Valică and Măriuca Onofreiu, you find something to give them, and give them more besides, don't you? I know all about it, you needn't think Smarandă is asleep, may you sleep for all eternity! So you've nothing to give for the boy? Shame, man, shame! You'll go to the bottomless pit of hell and you'll have no one to pull you out of it if you don't exert yourself to make your boy a priest. You flee from spooks like the devil flees from incense. You don't go to church from one Easter to another. Is that how you save your soul?"

"Come, be quiet, woman, church is in a man's heart, and when I come to die, I shall be taken to the church," said my father, "don't you talk so like that hypocritical Pharisee. You'd better put your hands on your breast, and say like the Publican, 'Lord, be merciful to me a sinner for I have abused my husband wrongfully.'"

Finally, however much my mother bickered with my father on my account she got the best of it, for one Sunday in Lent my mother's father, my grandfather, David Creangă from Pipirig, came to visit us, and seeing that a quarrel had broken out between my father and mother, he said:

"Come, Shtefan and my Smarandă, don't distress yourselves so, today is Sunday, tomorrow is Monday and market-day, but Tuesday, if I have my health, I will take my grandson with me, and send him to Broshteni with my Dumitru to Professor Nicolai Nanu of Balosh, and you shall see what he can make of the boy, for as for my other sons, Vasile and Gheorghe, I am very satisfied with what they've learned there. For twenty and more years, while I held the Office of tax collector in Pipirig, I with difficulty used tallies. What is the use of being able to read church manuals if one does not even know how to count; it's hard. So when my boys came from their schooling they kept my accounts penny by penny, and reckoned easily; I say now, one could be a tax collector for life, and not feel it. Truly, Alecu Balosh made a fine memorial for himself with that school of his for whoever knows its worth and, Lord, what an intelligent professor he discovered. He speaks so benignly, and receives with kindness everyone who is dear to one, and whom one sends to him. Happy the parents who gave birth to him, for he is an excellent man, I must say. Especially for our mountain peasants he is a great benefactor; when I came with my father, and my brothers, Petrea and Alexandru and Nică, from Transylvania to Pipirig, more than sixty years ago now, where could you have heard of a school like Balosh's in Moldavia? Perhaps at Jassy there was something of the kind, and at the Neamtzu Monastery during the time of the Metropolitan Iacob, who was a kind of kinsman of ours through Ciubuc the Bell-ringer at the Neamtzu Monastery; he was your mother's grandfather, Smarandă, and his name stands written to this day on the bell of Pipirig Church. Ciubuc, the Bell-ringer, also from Transylvania, had a little book-learning as also I had; he came from yonder like we did, and brought his belongings here like Mosh Dediu of Vânători, and others of our countrymen did, mostly on account of the Papists as far as I know. And so wealthy was he that the mountains, Halăuca, Iepure's Piatra, Bărnar, Cotnărel, and Boampele to the other side of Pătru-Vodă, were covered with his flocks and herds. And you must remember that Ciubuc was a man of integrity; every guest who entered his hall was received with hearty goodwill and entertained lavishly, and from all over the place came news of his kindness, and of his riches, until even the Prince once had himself taken to Ciubuc's house, and upon his asking him for whom he kept such a quantity of food, he replied: "For the weak in intellect and the strong in virtue, Your Highness." Then the Prince could not control his admiration, saying: 'Behold this man, say I; if there were more like him there would be little want in the country.' And the Prince slapped him on the shoulder, saying to him: 'My friend, know that from today on you are my man, and the doors of my Court are always open to you.' And from thenceforward, Ciubuc went by the name of 'the Prince's man,' while to this day a hill in the district towards Plotun, where Ciubuc lived a great deal, is called The Hill of the Man.

"On this hill, Smarandă, I took refuge during the revolution with your mother, with you and with your brother Ioan, for fear of a troop of Turks who were fighting just then with the Volunteers at Secu, and who then proceeded towards Pipirig after plunder. But in the hurry I was in I forgot your sister, little Marie, who was on the verandah in her cradle. When your mother discovered the child was missing, she began to tear her hair out of her head, and to sob beneath her breath, saying:

'Woe is me, woe is me, my child has been stabbed by the Turks.'

"But I climbed a fir tree, and when I saw the Turks making towards Plotun, I flung myself without more ado on to a horse bareback; I reached the house, and there I found the child safe and sound, only the cradle had been overturned by some pigs which were grunting round her as if they would tear her to pieces. But on the end of the cradle I found some gold pieces put by the Turks, it seems, by the child's head. Then I took the child and too happy to know how I did it, I reached your mother with her on the Hill of the Man. And when I had come to myself a little, I said in bitterness, as many have done before me: 'Those who have not children do not know what grief is.' And on that account some people have done well not to marry. And one among these was Ciubuc the Transylvanian, who having neither wife nor child, by reason of the great piety which came over him later in life, or for other reasons, consecrated all his fortune to the Monastery at Neamtzu, and he became a monk, and moreover all his servants with him, and he gave many alms as long as he was alive, but today he lies peacefully beside the monastery walls, may God have mercy on him, and give him rest in the heavenly kingdom! For tomorrow we too may go there. You would not bother about all this unless I told you about it," said grandfather, sighing.

"It's not a bad thing, Shtefan, for your boy to have a little book-learning, not particularly on account of the priesthood as Smarandă declares, for even priests have many anxieties which are hard to bear. And if you cannot be a good one, better not be one at all. But books bring you some kind of consolation. If I had not known how to read I should have been mad long ago with all I have had to bear. But I open the Lives of the Saints, and I see such and such, and I say, 'Lord, what resignation hast Thou given to Thine elect.' Our trials are nothing by the side of those they speak of in the books. And then for anyone to be entirely happy is not right. From books one learns much wisdom; and to tell the truth, only so can you be a man of use to everyone. I can see the boy has a good memory, and even after what he has learnt up to now he can sing and read as well as can be."

Of these and other things like them grandfather David talked to my father and mother all night Sunday till Monday, and Monday till Tuesday, for he always stayed with us when he came from Pipirig to the market to buy what he needed.

But on Tuesday he put the saddle and panniers on the horses, and gently tying the second horse by the bridle to the tail of the first one, and the third to the tail of the second, and the fourth to the tail of the third, he said:

"Well, Shtefan and dear Smarandă, good luck be with you, for I must be going. Come, grandson, are you ready?"

"Ready, grandfather, let's go," said I, tantalized by some cutlets of smoked pork, and fried sausages which my mother put in front of me. And taking farewell of my parents, I proceeded with my grandfather towards Pipirig. That morning there was a frost enough to spit wood. And above Vânători, as we crossed the bridge over the Neamtzu river, grandfather behind with the led horses, and I in front, my boots slipped and I fell into the Ozana stream; what a boy I was! Poor grandfather...

"Your boots have brought you ill-luck," said he,

quickly pulling me out; I was wet to the skin, and very cold, for the stream was swollen with ice, and hastily I took my boots off my feet for they were getting hard.

"A sandal is the best, boy! One's foot rests in it, and it is pleasant to wear in cold weather." Before he had finished speaking I was wrapped in a long-haired cloak, put into a pannier on one of the horses, and we continued on our road, and reached Pipirig. But when my grandmother saw what a state I was in, groaning in the pannier like a lost soul, she burst into tears. I have never seen a woman cry over things as she did; she was tender-hearted beyond measure. She ate no meat on this account, and when she went to festivals at the church she mourned for all the dead in the cemetery, whether relations or strangers, without distinction. But grandfather had a very well-regulated mind; he did all the jobs he understood and left grandmother to herself.

"Heavens, David, why aren't you more patient; how could you take the boy from home in this weather?"

"Just to surprise you, Nastasie," said grandfather, pulling a wild boar's skin out of the drawer, and cutting out two pairs of sandals for Dumitru and for me; then he folded them neatly, and passed a black thread of horsehair through the eyelets in each pair. The third day after this they gave us a change of linen, and two pairs of white cotton tapes for our legs; we put on our sandals carefully, and after kissing my grandmother's hand I took my way through Boboieshti, together with my grandfather and Dumitru, my mother's youngest brother; following the valley of Halăuca, we arrived rather late in Fărcasha, where we lodged with Father Dumitru from Câjia River, who had a goitre as big as a large gourd on his throat, and snored through it as through a pipe so that I could not close my eyes all night on his account. He could not help it, poor priest, and as he said, it is worse for those with a goitre in their head than those who wear one outside.

The next day we proceeded from Fărcasha by Borca towards the Câjia brook, and Cotârgash till we reached Broshteni. And after handing us over to a certain Irinuca, and paying all her charges, grandfather took us to see the Professor, and to the church, where we knelt before the Icons and finally he wished us luck, and returned home, sending us, from time to time, all that we required.

And the village of Broshteni, being scattered like nearly all the mountain villages, the wolves and the bears were not shy of showing themselves in it in broad daylight; there was a house in this ravine, there was a house the other side of the Bistritza in another ravine, I tell you, wherever man had found it convenient to make one. Irinuca had an old wooden hovel with windows like the palm of one's hand, roofed with boards and enclosed by a fence of pine, and situated right under the mountain on the left bank of the Bistritza, near the bridge. Irinuca was neither a young woman nor yet an old one, she had a husband, and so cross-eyed a daughter, that one was scared to spend the night with her in the house. Luckily, from early Monday till Saturday evening we did not see her; she went with her father to the mountains, and worked all the week like a man, and all for nothing, for two people, with two oxen, would hardly have been able to make enough in the winter time to buy polenta. And often it happened that they came back on Saturday night with a sprained ankle or bruised oxen, and that was all their gain.

The hovel on the left bank of the Bistritza, the husband, the daughter, and two oxen from the forest, a billy-goat, and two weak and mangy nanny-goats, which always slept in the passage, were Irinuca's whole fortune. But even this is a fortune when a person is in good health. But that's not my affair. Let's look after our own business.

We, after grandfather had departed, went next day to school, and the Professor, seeing we were wearing plaits, ordered one of the scholars to shave us. When we heard such a thing we began to cry floods of tears, and to pray to all the Saints not to allow them to mutilate us so. But you can imagine the Professor stood over us till they had shorn us close. Then he placed us in a form with other scholars, and gave us to learn according to our ability; among other things "The Angel has Praised" to learn by heart. We went on thus till mid Lent. And then one fine day we woke covered with scabs of mange caught from Irinuca's goats. Well, well, what was to be done?

The schoolmaster could no longer receive us at school, Irinuca would not cure us, we could not let my grandfather know, the provisions were nearly done, poor us! I don't know why but as the Feast of the Annunciation drew near it was unusually warm, and the snow melted, and the stream began to flow, and the Bistritza was swollen from bank to bank so that it nearly reached Irinuca's house. And during this warm weather we washed ourselves with the lees of the washing water, then we sat out of doors in the sun in our bare skins till the soap suds dried on us, and then we descended into the Bistritza to bathe. An old woman taught us this as a way of getting rid of the mange. You can picture to yourself what it meant to bathe in the Bistritza at Broshteni twice a day during Lent. We did not get pleurisy, or the ague, or any other disease, but neither did we get rid of the mange. One day when Irinuca had gone to the village, where it was her habit to sit for hours with the daughter of the mayor's assistant, there was mischief for us to do. We went up the hill above her house each with a log in his hand, and as the brooks were running strong, especially one which was as white as milk, the devil made us displace a rock which was just swaying, and the rock rolled down the hill, jumping as high as a man's stature, and passed through the fence, and through Irinuca's porch on to the goats, and straight into the Bistritza, making the water thunder. This was on Lazarus' Sunday, in the morning. Well, well, what was to be done? A woman's fence and house destroyed, a goat squashed to bits, is no joking matter. We forgot the mange and everything else in our fear.

"Quick, collect all your things before the old woman comes back, and let us escape on this raft to my brother Vasile at Borca," said Dumitru, for the raft began to move. You would have been amazed how we packed up the rest of our things, and ran fast to the raft, and pushed off like experienced raftsmen. What Irinuca said of us, or what she did not say, I know not, but I know this much, we were chilled to the marrow with fear until we reached Borca where we had dinner. And the next day, Palm Sunday, in the early morning we left Borca, and started across the Bătrân Range together with two frontier guards on horseback on the way to Pipirig. It was a beautiful day that Sunday, and the guards said they had never known such an early spring as this one.

I, and Dumitru too, went along singing, and gathering hepaticas and cyclamen on the mountainside, and we ran about, and sparred with each other just because we were no longer the mangy boys in Broshteni, who had given such pleasure in the house of Irinuca. And as we went along thus, about noon the beautiful weather changed into a frightful storm, and blew down fir trees, it was so violent. It began to drizzle, then to hail and blow, and finally turned cold, and snowed hard, and in a moment our path was barred so that we did not know in which direction to go. And the snow and fog came right down to the ground so that one could not see the person next one.

"The weather has changed for the worse," said one of the guards, sighing: "I was wondering at the winter leaving us so early. We have missed the road. From now on we must go at a venture, and where it has been ordained, there we shall arrive."

"One can hear the sound of a cock crowing," said the other guard. "Let us go in that direction, we may come upon a village somewhere."

And we descended, and continued to descend with difficulty down some precipitous places, and to stumble through clumps of pine trees, and the horses slipped and rolled, and I and Dumitru went along benumbed with cold, crying with our hands up to our faces while the guards heaved their chests, and bit their lips with cold and misery; the snow had drifted waist high at one point, and it had begun to grow dark when we reached an impassable place in the mountains where we could hear the sound of a rivulet which like ourselves was descending the mountains into the valley, invading and striking the rocks involuntarily... That was all, it passed on its way while we remained where we were, and ate polenta without any water.

"Eh, boys, this is where you'll have to snore to-night," said one of the guards, striking a light, and setting fire to a pine log.

"What has been decreed for you is written on your forehead, gaiety and good temper," said the other, pulling a big piece of polenta out of a pannier, roasting it on the embers, and giving each of us a handful. That polenta slipped down our throats as easily as if it had been made with butter! After we had eaten we crouched round the fire; there was snow above and damp underneath, one side of one was frozen, the other was burnt, according to the weather, and the place one was in. Miserable as we werc, yet another misfortune was to overtake us; the pine log petered out for want of care on the part of one of the guards. Perhaps Irinuca's curse reached us after all.

At last daylight came, and after washing ourselves with snow, and praying according to the custom of Christians, we moved on with the guards down the hill we were descending. The snow had already ceased, and after much trouble we found the road, and on and on, on and on! towards evening we reached grandfather David's house in Pipirig. And when grandmother saw us, she gave a cry of delight.

"My David means to bring me to my grave with his plans, I can see. Look what they have got on them, poor boys! How the mange has eaten them among strangers, poor things!"

And after she had pitied us, and cried over us according to her custom, and after she had given us to eat the best she had, and after she had washed us well, grandmother hurried off to her room, and brought out a pot of birch-resin, and smeared our bodies from top to toe, and then sent us to sleep in the warmth of the stove. And in the same way she anointed us two or three times a day, until on Good Friday we woke up completely cured. But in the meantime news had come from Broshteni of the damage we had done, and grandfather, without a word, had compensated Irinuca with four ducats. Then on Easter Saturday they sent me to my parents in Humuleshti. And on Easter Day I sang "The Angel has Praised" in church so that everyone sat open-mouthed. And Father Ioan invited me to luncheon with him, and Esmeralda cracked a great many red eggs with me. And pleasure after pleasure fell to my share. But the second Mass did not go so well; all the girls in the village came to church, and some of them, feeling mischievous already, when they caught sight of me, burst out laughing and began to make fun of me just because my hair had been cut.

# CHAPTER II

I DO NOT know how others may be, but I, when I think of the place where I was born, of my father's house in Humuleshti, of the pillar of the chimney-piece to which my mother tied a string with some bows of ribbon on the end of it, and which the cats played with till they nearly died, of the lime-washed buttress of the hearth to which I clung when I began to walk, of the oven where I hid when we boys played games, and other pranks, full of childlike fun and charm, my heart seems even now to jump for joy. And Heavens, it was pleasant then, for my parents, and my brothers and sisters were well, and the house was well provisioned, our neighbors' boys and girls were continually playing with us, and they all did my pleasure, without any ill will, exactly as if the world was mine.

And I was as bright as fine weather, and as mild and willful as the wind when it blows.

My mother, who was renowned for her wonder working, said to me sometimes with a smile, when the sun began to come out from behind the clouds after a prolonged rain, "Go out, fair-haired child and laugh at the sun, perhaps that will change the weather." And the weather changed after I had laughed... You see the sun knew with whom he had to deal, I was my mother's son; indeed, she could perform many and great wonders; she could turn the black clouds away from our village, and divert the hail to other districts, by striking a hatchet into the ground in front of our door; she could make water freeze with the aid of only two cows' feet while people crossed themselves with wonder; she would beat the ground, or the wall or any piece of wood against which I had struck my head, or hand, or leg, saying "Na, na!" and at once the pain passed off...

When the burning charcoal crackled in the stove, which they say means wind and rough weather, or when the charcoal hissed, which shows that someone is talking ill of you, my mother would scold it there on the hearth, and pinch it with tongs to destroy the enemy, and even more than this, if my mother did not like my looks, with a finger wet with saliva, she would at once prepare a little of the mud from the sole of my boot, or hastily just take some soot from the mouth of the stove, saying, "Just as the mouth of the stove cannot be hurt by the evil eye so may not the evil eye hurt my child!" And then she would smear my forehead with soot so that nothing could injure her pet, and many similar things did she do.

Such was my mother during my childhood, full of marvels which come to my mind, and I remember well, for her arms cradled me when I fed at hear breast, gurgling and looking lovingly into her eyes.

She gave me blood of her blood, flesh of her flesh, from her I learned to talk, from her I gained knowledge of God, when the time came to distinguish right and wrong.

But time slipped sweetly by, and I gradually grew up, and other thoughts crowded through my brain, and other pleasures awoke in my heart, and instead of being wiser I grew more turbulent, and now my desire was beyond bound: so captivating and deceiving is a man's thought, carrying him on the wings of a ceaseless longing, which never leaves him in peace till he enters the grave.

But woe betide the man who lets sad thoughts take hold of him; take care, you get carried unwittingly into deep water, and from the greatest happiness fall at once into a painful sadness.

Come, it's better to talk of childhood for that only is happy, and innocent. Frankly, that's the truth.

What does the child care when mother and father are thinking of the difficulties of life, of what tomorrow may bring, or are turning over in their minds other thoughts full of worry? The child astride his stick thinks he is mounted upon a most fiery horse which races gladly along, and he beats it with his whip, and reins it in when he wishes, and shouts at it with all his heart, enough to deafen one, and when he falls down he thinks the horse has thrown him, and pours out his fury upon the stick with all the words and his command.

Such a child was I at that happy age, and so I think have all children been ever since this world was made; people may say what they like.

When my mother could work no more she was so weary, and went to rest for part of the day, we boys just began to raise the roof. When my father came back in the evening from the Dumesnicu forest, frozen with cold, and covered with hoar-frost, we frightened him by jumping on his back in the dark. And he, tired as he was, would capture us one after the other, as in "catch-who-catch-can," and throw us up to the ceiling, and kiss us over and over again. After father had lit the lamp, and begun to eat, we drew the cats out from the nook by the oven, and beat them and drilled them in front of him till they were at the last gasp, and the poor cats could not escape out of our hands till they scratched us and spat at us.

"So you look on, man," said my mother, "and let them do as they like, is that it? Ha, ha! Serves you well, little ruffians that you are, not a beast can take shelter near this house on account of your cruelty. Because I've not smacked you today you tease those cats, but man like dog learns through the stick. I'll fetch the birch-rod and give you a thrashing."

"Come, wife, let them alone, they are glad because I've come back," said father, jumping us up and down on his knee. "What do they care, there are logs in the shed, enough lard and flour in the loft, cheese in the barrel, and cabbage in the crock, thank God! They just want to be healthy enough to eat and play while they are little; their lightheartedness will pass when they are bigger, and worries will come to them;

don't be afraid they will escape them. Don't you know this proverb: 'a child plays, a horse pulls, a priest reads...' "

"Easy for you to say, man," said my mother, "you don't have to stay in the house all day with them, it's enough to turn one's hair white, if only the earth would swallow them up, God forgive me. If only the summer would come so that they might play outside, for I'm as sick of them as of crab-apples. They do any mischief that comes into their heads; when they begin to strike the hour of service at the church your good Zaha runs outside, and rattles the loom enough to shake the walls of the house, and break the windows. While that harum-scarum Ion with the sheep-bell and the tongs and the poker makes such a hubbub and row as to deafen one; then they each put a rug on their backs, and a paper cap on their heads, and sing "Hallelujah, God have mercy, the priest catches fish," till it drives one out of the house. And this happens two or three times every day, and one ought to give them a good whipping if one gave them what they deserve."

"Come, come, woman, you're famed for your love of church, at least the boys have made a church here for your pleasure; you can even go to church in the house instead of at a distance."

"Well, where's your common sense, man, I'm surprised the youngsters are as good as they are when you approve of their ways, and back them up. See how they stand all wide awake and stare at us as if they mean to draw us. When they have to get up and work you should see how they dawdle and sulk and grumble," said mother. "Go to bed, boys, the night is going; what do you care as long as you have food under your noses!"

And when we were all in bed, we boys, just like boys, began to fight each other, and could not sleep for excitement, until poor mother was surely obliged to give us some raps on the head, and some blows on the back. And father, getting tired sometimes of so much noise, would say to mother:

"Silence, silence, that's enough for now, colts!"

And then mother would give us more cuffs, and harder ones, saying:

"I'll give it to you, you little devils! I can't sleep at nights because of your laughter."

And only so could poor mother get relief from our naughtiness; she was to be pitied! But you don't think she got off as easily as that, do you?

First thing the next morning we began again, and mother took down the birch-rod from the beam, and beat us again, but do you think we took much heed of that?

And all that passed through our heads, and all we did with such energy I can recall to mind as though it were happening now. Remember all these things if you can and if your memory serves you, Ion.

At Christmas when father killed the pig, and singed and boiled it and quickly wrapped it in straw to make it easier to skin, I used to mount it outside the straw, and make a great racket, knowing I should be given the pig's tail when it was cold, and the bladder to fill with grain and blow out and drum upon when it was dry, and then, woe betide my mother's ears until she boxed mine. And one story I must not forget; one St. Basil's Day we collected some boys from the village, and went from house to house with our barrow and sang carols; I am older now, alas! The eve of St. Basil I worried my father all day to make me a drum, or at any rate to let me have a whip to crack, and join the carol singers.

"Lord, what a whipping I'll give you," said my father. "Haven't you anything to eat at home? Do you want these ne'er-do-wells to drag you through the snow? Now, take your boots off!"

Seeing I had made a false step over this I slipped out of the house with just the pig's bladder so that my father would not take my boots, and I should not be put to shame before my comrades. I don't know how it happened but one of my companions had a bell. My sheep-bell was at home, but how could I go and get it? Finally, we did the best we could, and collected a broken sickle from one place, the hook of a yoke from another, besides a poker with a ring, and my pig's bladder, and we began to play a tune, and went from house to house. We betook ourselves to Father Oshlobanu at the top of the town with the idea of going through the whole place... The priest was cutting up logs out of doors; when he saw us arrange ourselves in front of the window, and prepare to carol he began to abuse us, and say:

"Lord, the chickens have hardly gone to roost when you begin. But stay a minute, you wretches, and I'll give you what for!"

We took to flight. But he rushed after us with a big stick, so gruff and violent a man was Father Oshlobanu. And from fright we ran back half-way through the town without having recited this rhyme to the priest, as is the custom for carol-singers to do at the houses where they get nothing:

"Fungus on the floor boards,
Toadstools on the walls,
As many feathers on the cock,
As there are hungry children."

"Oh, what a worthless and nasty priest," we said when we had all assembled, frozen with cold and fear; he nearly destroyed us, the furious creature; we should like to see him carried on a bier to the church of St. Dumitru, below the castle, where he takes the services, and while we grumbled to each other it grew quite dark.

Well, now, what was to be done?

"We must go into this yard," said Zaharia Gâtlan, "for we are wasting time standing in the middle of the road."

And we went into Vasile Anitza's yard, and stood near the window as is the custom. But things seemed bewitched; one could not strike the sickle because he was cold; another's hands were stiff with cramp, my cousin Ion Mogorogea, with the poker under his arm, refused to carol, it was enough to break one's heart!

"You sing, Chiriac," said I to Goian, "and we, Zaharia, will roar like a bull while the others shout 'hi, hi!' "

And we began all together. Then what happened? What must that parsimonious wife of Vasile Anitza do but run after us with a red hot poker, for just at that moment she was going to make up the fire for her cakes in the oven.

"The fire will eat you; may it catch you!" said she, much excited, "what do you mean by this? Where did you learn such impudence?"

Then we fled, we boys, faster than from Father Oshlobanu.

"This has been a failure," we said when we stopped at the crossroads in the center of the town, near the church.

"A little more of this sort of thing, and the men will throw us out of the village like so many gypsies. Much better go to bed." And after we had pledged ourselves with an oath to go out again all together at the New Year we separated, stiff with cold, and faint from hunger, and each one went to his home, which seemed a very good plan. And that is how we went carol-singing that year.

Then what a mess I made of the cream in the bowls.

When mother had put the milk to set, I began to lick the cream off the bowls the next day, and so on each day till I left only skimmed milk. When mother tried to skim the bowls, well, skim away Smarandă, if you have anything to skim!

"Perhaps the vampires have stolen the milk from the cows, little Mother," said I, curling up on the floor near the bowls, with my tongue hanging out.

"I'll catch that vampire at the bowl one time, with cream," said my mother looking searchingly at me, "and then we'll see. The birch-rod shall be told of it, and not all the family of vampires and vampiresses in the world shall pull it out of my hand. One can always tell the vampire that has eaten cream by his tongue. All my life I've detested the false and fawning person, I tell you straight, my pet, and you take it from me, God never helps one who is deceitful, whether it be in a matter of importance or a matter of food, or whatsoever it may be."

Mother knows something, I say to myself, for I wasn't so silly as to not understand such things.

Then again with Mosh Chiorpec, the cobbler and our neighbor, what trouble I had... that is to say, speaking truthfully, what trouble he had with me, for I went to the man many times, and worried him to give me thongs with which to make a whip.

And how many times I found Mosh Chiorpec rubbing the boots with the best white resin which made the leather as soft as cotton. And when the man saw he could not get rid of me with words he took me gently by the chin with his left hand while with the right he drew the stick from the crock containing the resin, and gave me a nice streak of grease across my mouth so that all the apprentices in the shop roared with laughter. And when he let me go I ran home to my mother, crying and spitting

38

to right and left.

"See, Mother, what that fiend Chiorpec has done to me!"

"I should have done the same," said my mother, calmly, "I shall thank him when I meet him; you are so persistent wherever you go, and drive people wild with your pranks, idler that you are."

When I heard this I washed my mouth quickly and said no more about it... And when I forgot my grievance I ran again to Mosh Chiorpec for some thongs; and when he saw me come in at the door he said with delight: "Ha, ha, welcome, my boy." And once more he painted me, and made fun of me, and once more I tore home crying, spitting, and swearing, and my mother was worried about me because of this.

"Ugh! If winter would only come you might be sent to school somewhere," said my mother, "and I would ask the school master to give you such a thrashing there would be nothing left of you."

Once, one summer near the time of the Great Fair, I stole out of the house in broad daylight, and went to Mosh Vasile's house, he was my father's eldest brother, to steal some cherries, for only at his house, and in one or two other places in the village, were there early cherries ripe by Pentecost. And I was turning over in my mind how I would behave in order not to get caught. First of all I went into the man's house, and asked for Ion to come for a swim.

"Ion is not at home," said Aunt Mariora, "he has gone with your Uncle Vasile down below the castle to a mill from Condreni to fetch some cloaks."

For I must tell you that in Humuleshti all the girls and boys and women and men weave, and make many woolen cloaks and a grey woolly material, besides serge and embroidered stuffs which they sell on the spot to Armenian traders who come especially from other market towns, such as Focshani, Băcău, Roman, Târgu-Frumos and elsewhere, and also at fairs all over the place. Many of the people of Humuleshti who were small landholders deprived of their fields made their living in this way and by trading in a variety of things, such as cattle, horses, pigs, sheep, cheese, wool, oil, salt and maize meal; cloaks, long, short, and three-quarter length; summer trousers, pantaloons, silk chemises, skirts and aprons embroidered with flowers; fine fichus of gauze, and other things, which they took to the market on Monday to sell, or on Thursday to the convent of nuns who found it rather difficult to get to the market.

"Good day, Aunt Mariora. As I said just now I am sorry Cousin Ion is not at home, it would have been great fun to bathe together." But I thought to myself: "Aren't I in luck? It's good he's not at home, and it will be much better if he doesn't come back too soon..."

And quickly and affectionately I kissed my aunt's hand, and taking my leave like a good boy, I left the house as if I were going to bathe. I crept along where I could, and reached the cherry tree, and began to stuff the cherries into my shirt, unripe and ripe just as they came. And as I was fussing and trying to be as quick as I could there comes Aunt Mariora along the trunks of the cherry trees with a little birch-rod in her hand!

"That's good, you rascal, is that how you bathe?" she said, with eyes glaring at me, "come down, you thief, and I'll learn you!"

But why get down when destruction awaits you below! When she looked up and saw that I was not giving in, whirr! She threw clods of earth at me several times, but I took no heed. Then she began to climb the cherry tree, saying: "Look out, you glutton, Mariora will catch you now!" Then I sprang quickly on to a low bough, and jumped down into some flax, which stretched away in front of the cherry trees; it was not yet ripe, and came up to one's waist, and after me came furious Aunt Mariora. I tore through the flax, and she behind me, up to the fence at the bottom of the garden; not having time to jump it, I doubled back again through the flax, running like a hare, and she after me, up to the right side of the enclosure, where again it was difficult for me to jump, and along the side of the fence, while my famous aunt did not slacken in her pursuit of me. If only she could lay hands on me! And I ran, and she ran, and I ran and she ran until we had laid the flax flat with the earth, for it's no lie to say there were ten to twelve perches of beautiful flax quite destroyed, and rendered useless. And when we had finished this work, my aunt, I don't know how, slipped in the flax, or caught in something and fell...

Then I turned on my heel, gave one or two bounds, threw myself over the fence without touching it, and was lost to sight; I ran home and was very good all day...

But later in the evening Mosh Vasile appeared with the sheriff, and the sentry. He called to father from the door and told him the matter, and insisted upon him being present when an examination was made of the flax and cherry trees. Truth to tell, Mosh Vasile was a miser, and a curmudgeon, and Aunt Mariora was too.

In vain I squeaked, "What have you to do with the man's affairs?" The damage was done, and the fault had to be paid for. As the proverb says: "The rich do not pay but the guilty do." And so father paid the fine for me, and peace was restored. When he came back ashamed from the examination he gave me a wigging, saying:

"Na! Stuff yourself with cherries! But know that henceforth I shall not believe in you, gallows bird! How much damage am I to pay for on your account?"

And thus in the case of the cherries, mother's words were fulfilled quickly, and hurriedly, poor thing: "God does not help those who walk deceitfully." But what's the good of repentance after death? How ashamed I was, what could I do with myself? How could I meet Aunt Mariora, or Mosh Vasile, or Cousin Ion, or even the boys and girls from the village; especially on Sunday at church, or at the dance, which is so pretty to watch, or at the bathing-place which is the tryst of all the young men and maidens who pine for each other all the week while at work.

I tell you everyone knew of the prank I had played, and I had not the audacity to face the world, I was so ashamed, particularly when some pretty girls from the village came up to our house, and made my heart beat fast. As the saying goes:

"Well, Ion, you are fond of the girls!"

"I am."

"And they of you?"

"And I of them."

But what was to be done? This passed off like other things; audacity carried it off, and least said soonest mended like so many other things that happened to me in life... not in one year nor in two, but from time to time, and through a long series of years.

And if I vowed to myself never to play a prank again, the devil seemed to egg me on, and I did it with zest. Directly after the affair with the cherries came something else.

One morning early my mother roused me roughly from my sleep, saying, "Get up, you sluggard, before the sun rises; do you want the hoopoe to "pup-pup", and bring you bad luck so that nothing goes right all day?"

Thus my mother used to threaten us with a hoopoe which for many years had made its nest in a very old and hollow lime tree on the side of the hill at Mosh Andrew's, father's youngest brother's place. One heard nothing all the summer but "Pu-pu-pup!

Pu-pu-pup!" from first thing in the morning, and daily, till the village echoed. When I was up my mother at once sent me off into the country with the victuals for some wooden-spoon makers who were working for us just then in the Saca Valley close to Topolitza. As I went along with the food I heard nothing but the hoopoe:

"Pu-pu-pup! Pu-pu-pup! Pu-pu-pup!"

Now why didn't I keep straight on my way? I turned off towards the lime tree with the idea of capturing the hoopoe, for I was very anxious about it, because I was roused every day at dawn on account of it. And when I arrived at the lime tree, I put the dinner down on the road on the hill, climbed cautiously up the tree, stupefied by the fragrance of its flowers; I put my hand into the hollow which I had reached, and by good luck I felt the hoopoe on its eggs; full of gratitude, I said: "So, my friend, I have caught you, you shall never 'pup-pup' again." But when I was about to pull out the bird, I don't know why, I was frightened of its crest of ruffled feathers for I had never seen a hoopoe before, and I let it go in the hollow. I stayed still, and decided in my mind that it could not well be a serpent with feathers... although according to what I had heard from people serpents were sometimes found in hollows... however, I would not let myself be put off, and again I put in my hand to seize the hoopoe... if it were one; but it, poor thing, evidently was hiding in some crevice in the hollow for fear of me, for nowhere could I lay hands on it; it seemed to have disappeared in the ground. "Well this is a curious thing," said I, anxiously taking off my cap, and stuffing up the mouth of the hole with it; then down I got, found a suitable bit of wood, climbed up the tree again with it, took out my cap, and put the bit of wood in its place, thinking to myself that the hoopoe would reappear from somewhere by the time I returned from the plain. After this I descended again, and proceeded quickly with the workmen's dinner... But however fast I went, time had been lost while I was wandering out of my way, goodness knows where, and hunting about and struggling in the lime tree to try and catch the hoopoe, and the spoon-makers, their ears pricked with hunger, that's the only way I can describe them, were waiting. A proverb says: "The gypsy sings when he is hungry, the boyar walks with his hands behind him, but our peasants light their pipes and sulk." Thus it was with our spoon-makers; they sang like lunatics on the plain, sitting by the side of the ditch, their eyes misty from staring to see whether their food was coming or not. Then, towards midday they saw only me standing on a mound with the food all dried up, not daring to come on when I heard them grumbling so fiercely. They jumped upon me like dragons, and would have devoured me if there had not been a jolly girl among them who took my part: "Hey, shut up, why blame the boy, have it out with his father but not with him." After this the men took no notice of me, but fell upon the food in sulky silence. But I, escaping with a whole skin, took the bag with the plates and dishes, and started towards the town; I reached the lime tree again, climbed up it, put my ear to the mouth of the hole, and heard something beating about inside; then I took out the bit of wood, carefully put in my hand, and drew out the hoopoe exhausted with the struggle, but when I tried to take the eggs they were all squashed. After this I went home, fastened the hoopoe by the leg with a string, and hid it from my mother for a couple of days in the loft among some battered bee hives; every so often I went to the hoopoe, making the people of the house wonder why I went to the loft so often. But the day after this, Aunt Mariora, Mosh Andrew's wife, came to our house in a towering rage, and began quarreling with my mother on my account:

"Just listen, sister, such a thing as this, Ion to steal the hoopoe which has woken us up at daybreak to work for so many years," said my aunt sadly. She was terribly upset, and nearly cried when she said this. And then I saw that my aunt was very right, the hoopoe was the village clock. But my mother, poor thing, had no idea of all this.

"What are you talking about, sister-in-law? I'd thrash him to death if I found he's caught the hoopoe, and teased it. You are right to tell me, rely upon me, I'll box his ears for him."

I, being hidden in the room, when I heard these words mounted into the loft, took the bird from where it was, jumped from the eaves of the house with it, and went straight off to the cattle-market to sell it, for it just happened to be a Monday, and market day. When I reached the fair I began to strut up and down among the people with the hoopoe in my hand, for in a way I, too, was a merchant's son. A silly old man with a heifer on a string and nothing to do, said:

"Is that chicken for sale, my boy?"

"It is for sale, old man."

"What do you want for it?"

"How much do you think?"

"Come, give it here to the old man, and let him feel the weight."

As I gave it into his hand the sulky old devil examined it for an egg, and gently took the string off its leg, then he threw it up in the air, saying: "What a pity, I lost it!" Whirr! Went the hoopoe on to the top of a booth, and after resting there a while took flight towards Humuleshti, and left me for good and all with tears on my cheeks, gazing after it. I caught the old man by his cloak to make him pay me for the bird.

"What's your idea, old man? You trifle with a man's goods? Even if you did not want to buy it, why did you let it go? You and your heifer won't escape me like that. Do you understand? It's no joke." And I glared at the old man, and made such a row that people gathered round us, like they do at a play, for it was fair-time.

"You know you're rather hard on life, boy," said the old man, laughing. "What do you rely on that you dare to be so impertinent, young man? Say, would you perchance like to take my heifer in exchange for your hoopoe? I think you're looking for a thrashing, young'un, and here's one for you if you want it; but if I give you a flogging I fancy you'll cry 'Mercy' before you escape from my hands."

"Let the lad alone," said one of our men from Humuleshti, "he's the son of Shtefan Petre, a citizen of our town and you'll get into grave trouble with him over this..."

"Ha, ha! Good luck to you, good man, do you think I don't know Shtefan Petre?" said the old fellow, "only just now I saw him walking through the market with a measure under his arm after he had bought his cloth which was his business here; he ought to be somewhere, or in some inn drinking the lucky cup. It's a good thing I know who you are, young'un, isn't it? In a few minutes I can take you to your father, and see whether he sent you with a hoopoe to sell and spoil the fair."

However, when I heard talk of my father my mouth grew dry, I slipped quietly through the crowd, and made full speed for Humuleshti; looking back to be sure the old man did not overtake me, for now I only wanted to escape from him, truth to tell. A proverb says: "Let be! I would lose him but I see he won't lose me!" I had been unfortunate, but still I was glad to have escaped with nothing worse. "What luck if I could carry the thing through like this with mother and Aunt Mariora," thought I, with my heart beating like a hare's from fright and fatigue. But when I got home I found that father and mother had gone to the market, and my brother told me with alarm what a fuss there was with Mosh Andrew's wife, and almost the whole town was roused over the hoopoe from the lime tree; it was said we had taken it, and mother was very angry about this.

"You know Aunt Mariora is one of those people who can make a drunken man sober; that's a fact."

And as they were telling me this so anxiously we heard singing in the lime tree:

"Pu-pu-pup! Pu-pu-pup! Pu-pu-pup!"

And then Catrina, my sister, said with surprise:

"Listen, all of you! Lord, how unjustly some people accuse a person when he is in the right!"

"That's so, little sister!" But inwardly I thought, "Did you but know what it has suffered on my account, and I on its account, you would weep with pity."

But Zaha left us talking and went to the market after mother to tell her the joyful tidings about the hoopoe. And the second day of March, just on the last day before the fast of St. Peter, mother baked a quantity of maize-meal tarts and cakes and wheat-meal rolls, and roasted on the spit some tender-young chickens, which she rolled in butter, for our early dinner, and invited Aunt Mariora to come to us, and said to her kindly:

"Gracious, sister-in-law, how people quarrel about nothing at all when they believe what evil tongues say! But if you please, sister, it is much better to eat of what God has given us, and drink a glass of wine to the good health of our fellow citizens.

" 'May all things harmful be dispersed,

And all good things increased
Let all ill-will between us cease,
And the land be free from tares.'

If you are going to make bad blood over everything, indeed the time will come when you'll take leave of your senses."

"That is so, dear sister-in-law," said Aunt Mariora, shrugging her shoulders with embarrassment, as she seated herself at the table, "you'll see another time I shall not believe what people say."

Then we all began to eat; I don't know about the others, but I do know I made a good meal, enough for the whole day. And directly I had got up from the table, making my escape, I hurried off to bathe, and when I valiantly jumped into the pool from a high bank I accidentally fell face downwards so that I saw stars from pain, and I really thought I had burst, neither more nor less. After I had got out of the water with great difficulty, and clinging to friendly hands, had pulled myself on to the bank, the boys made a group around me, and buried me in sand, and said the prayers for the dead over me as well as they knew how, and I was scarcely conscious for over an hour; I began to bathe undisturbed until sunset; I contrived to go home with the cows, and told mother that our herdsman had deserted the yard at midday, and so I alone had taken them to pasture, and on that account I had been delayed till now. And mother, good soul, believing them all to be in milk, after the tale I had told her with caresses, praised me for the useful thing I had done, and gave me something to eat. I devoured my food, and looked modest while inwardly I was laughing; marveling even then at the subtlety of the lies I improvised till I almost came to half-believe them myself.

And so can man many times deceive himself even when he does not intend to, unless he has learned to judge soundly. But all the same I say:

"All suffering buys experience."

One day towards the feast of St. Elias, there had accumulated as usual a mass of work for mother to do; some pieces of material to take off the loom; others to unravel and weave anew; a pile of stuff up to the ceiling cut out, and waiting to be sewn; the cards of wool on the benches had no one to wind them off; bobbins to put on the spinning-wheel, one baby in the cradle, and five or six others waiting for something to eat; it was work, not play, and also it needed haste, for the Fălticeni Fair was coming fast; and that was that. And mother roused me earlier than usual, and said to me affectionately:

"Nică, my pet, your father has gone to reap, for the oats are dropping and as usual I can hardly see out of my eyes for work so you must give up running about, and stay with Mother, and wind the bobbins, and rock the baby, and then I'll bring you a straw hat with a ribband from Fălticeni, and an overall with a leather belt, all for yourself."

"All right, Mother," but only I knew what was in my mind. All the same, at the sewing and embroidering of the cloaks, and especially at the spinning, I tried to surpass the elder girls who spun, and on this account naughty Măriuca Săvucu, whom to tell you the truth I did not find ugly, sometimes grew angry with me, and slapped me, nicknaming me "Ion Torcălău", a name she got from some gipsy from Vânători. But she was all the dearer to me on this account, and I wound with her, in the shade of their walnut tree, such a heap of bobbins of thread that mother embraced me when she came home at night.

We boys and girls took our work to each other's houses that we might not get tired of it, and these meetings, called in the country reunions, took place chiefly at night, each person doing his own work; how much more willingly I worked in rivalry with Măriuca, and as the spindles whirled round and round so did my heart whirl round for love of Măriuca! God be my witness! And I remember that once, one night at the stripping of the maize, I snatched from Măriuca's bosom a mouse which would have sent the poor girl out of her mind if I had not been there. And then in summer, on holidays, who would not walk with the girls across the plain, over the hills, and especially through the meadows and the woods full of beauty, to gather osiers already turning yellow, marjoram in full bloom, balm mint, and melilot to put among the clothes!

The song says:

"Give me, Lord, a wealth of limes
And the society of women."

To put it shortly, where there were three, I was the fourth.

But when I heard talk of rocking the cradle I don't know what came over me! I had just the ill-luck of being the elder of the two brothers. What was there to do when mother begged? But the day she asked me the sky was so clear, and it was so lovely, and hot outside, one could bask in the warmth like the hens. When I saw such weather I went off to the pool thinking hard things of mother, for I was irritated with her. It's true God is over all! After a time mother, believing me to be somewhere in the fields, came out and began to shout with all her might, "Ion, Ion, Ion," but Ion held his tongue. When she found there was no answer from anywhere, she dropped everything, and followed me to the pool where she knew I was in the habit of going, and when she got there, she saw me rolling naked in the sand, just like a boar; I was standing holding to my ear a pebble burning from the sun, and with streaks of silver in it, I jumped first on one leg, and then on the other, then I bent my head to the right, and then to the left, reciting the words:

"Gold, tar,
Draw water to my ear,
And I will give you coins old,
And I will wash buckets for you,
And I will beat drums for you."

After this I threw a succession of stones into the deep pool where I bathed, one for the Lord, and one for the devil, quite impartially for both; then I threw something to imprison the devil at the bottom of the pool with lumps in his mouth; and then pouf! Into the pool went I, a plunge to catch the devil by one leg as is our custom when we bathe, since the time of Adam-Babadam. After this I plunged three times in succession, once for the Father, Son and Holy Ghost, and then once more for Amen. Then I drew myself up gently on the edge of the bank, for it amused me to watch on the sly how the water played over the pretty feet of some girls who were washing linen in the river above me. A prettier occupation I think one cannot see! All this time poor mother was watching, looking on from a rising of sand and pebbles on the shore, she had crossed her arms like an angry person does, and was close to me. All told, half an hour had passed while my mother waited there, but it was three-quarters of an hour since I had escaped from the house, and I ought to have been famished, as they say, it was so long past midday. But I, in the state in which I was, full of happiness, forgot that I was living in this world. At last mother, patient though she was, lost her temper, and came on tip-toe up behind me when I was watching the girls, as I told you, and quietly took away all my clothes from the bank, leaving me naked in the pool, saying to me bitterly:

"You'll come home, my wanderer, when you're overcome with hunger, and then I'll have something to say to you!" And off she went.

"Oh, oh, what will Ion do now?" The girls who were washing, and saw all this, gave each other a nudge, and laughed at my expense till the banks rang. I sank down with shame and might have drowned, so angry was I; and after all the great joy of a short time previously, now I could have strangled myself, neither more nor less. But a proverb says: "Can you stop wind, water, or men's tongues?" And so I let those girls laugh till their mouths stretched from ear to ear, and spying the time when they were bending over to put the linen into the water to wash, I sprang out of the pool, and took to my heels, and tore so fast along the bank that I made the stones jump as I spurned them with my feet. And on and on, without ever looking back, until I struck the lanes leading into the road that took us home. I did not follow the road for shame in case I met someone, but I jumped into Costache's garden, and bending down crept through the maize; then along a path in Trăsnea's garden, and again through the maize, and just as I was leaving the garden I realized that Trăsnea's dogs would set upon me. What was I to do? I had heard from someone that if you did not want dogs to bite you, but to leave you alone, when you see them spring at you, you must throw yourself to the ground, and without moving from the spot, let them bark at you as much as they like; they bay and bay, and after a while they leave you and go off. And it's true because that's how I escaped from Trăsnea's dogs then, when I had the ill-luck to meet them, and they me. It was the greatest good fortune that that giant and thief, Trăsnea who had a great grudge against me since he caught me in his garden stealing pears, did not catch me, or he would have thrashed me. And I really deserved even that, I was such a miserable sinner! At last, after Trăsnea's dogs had left me in peace, as I told you, I jumped across a road, and from there into our garden, and it seemed to me then that I was safe in God's keeping. And I went now without hiding through the maize till I came right up to the courtyard, and I looked through the fence, and saw mother flying about her work, now in the house, now outside; I was very sorry for her but also I was very sorry for my stomach which was full of water. The proverb says: "I am sorry for you, but my heart is breaking with pity for myself." And no longer able to bear the pangs of hunger I began to whisper humbly through the fence: "Mommy, here I am." And I immediately jumped into the courtyard, and placed myself in front of Mother naked as I was, seized her hand firmly, and kissing it, said, plaintively: "Mother, beat me, slay me, hang me, do what you like with me, only give me something to eat, for I am dying with hunger." The proverb says: "Nakedness beats about the bush but hunger goes straight to the goal." Then mother, for she was so good, looked sadly at me and said, sighing: "It looks well for a big boy like you to be wandering about the road in this state, and leaving me just at this time without a scrap of help! You may go and eat, but you know I've had enough of you; perhaps if you behave very well from now on I may feel for you again as I did before, but I don't know."

To put it shortly, when I saw I was in the wrong with mother I swore I would never again do what I had done; I followed her about quite gently, and never disobeyed her wishes either by deed or word, for a gentle word effects great things; at work I was as industrious as could be; I tidied and dusted the house like a grown-up girl so that mother need not worry when she went out anywhere.

Then one day she kissed me and said sweetly:

"God grant you length of days, little Ion, my pet, and give you all His richest gifts if you behave as I see you have been behaving for some time now."

Then I began to cry at once, and my joy was not insincere. Inwardly I had never felt such self-reproach as then. If mother had beaten me and turned me from the house like a stranger I should not have felt so humiliated before her as I did now when she treated me gently. And you need not think I did not keep my word from that Tuesday on for a long time, for I am like that, persevering and tenacious of my word after my own manner. I don't praise myself, the fact is there; when it was time to sleep I did not ask for food; If I got up I did not wait for others to get it for me, and when there was work to be done outside I rarely came back to the house. Then I had other characteristics: when anyone treated me roughly they got but little work out of me, when they treated me gently not very much, but when they let me be I carried out good little bits of work such as even St. Nastasia, the deliverer from poison, couldn't disarrange with all her cunning. The proverb says: "A fool can throw a stone into a pool, but ten wise men cannot pull it out."

But, finally, why so many words about nothing?

Well, even I have been in this world a ball with eyes, a piece of animated clay from Humuleshti, but I did not succeed in being good looking by the time I was twenty, or sensible by the time I was thirty, or rich by the time I was forty. But as poor as this year, or last year, or all the other years I never have been!

# CHAPTER III

"I SHOULD NOT mind if you were worth anything," said my conscience, "but ball with eyes that you are, piece of animated clay from our village, your heart does not let you keep silence; you dazzle the world with your peasant talk."

"It does not let me, indeed, keep silence; and why should it?"

I also am a man formed from two beings, and the village of Humuleshti where I saw the light is not an isolated village, dull and deprived of all amenities like other villages; and the places surrounding our village are also worthy of notice. Up above Humuleshti comes Vânători Neamtzu with the descendants of those men who once fought Sobieski, King of Poland. And still higher are the monasteries of Secu and Neamtzu, in other days the glory of the Romanian Church and the second treasury of Moldavia. Below come the villages of Boishtea, and of the Ghindăonians who harness Hungarian oxen only to their wagons; where the ploughs are left in the furrows in the fields for weeks, where the beehives have no keeper, where the newly sown ground has no sentry, yet no one injures them; the men of those villages do not know what a court of law is; next to Boishtea comes the village of Bleba where, if one drops one's cap into the water half the people say: "that's lost for the soul of your father." Towards the southwest lie the monasteries, Agapia, secluded from the world; and Văratic, where the rich and charitable Princess Brâncoveanu spent her days, and the village of Filioara, refuge of the two-legged roe-deer escaped from the monastery, the village of Băltzăteshti so full of wit, and the village of the Ceahlăieshtians, and Topolitza, and Ocea, where they chase the crow with a prune in its mouth just over the frontier; while towards the northeast beyond Ozana come the market town of Neamtzu, with its suburb Pometea under Cociorva Hill where every house stands in its own large orchard; and the Tutzuenians from Transylvania, who eat rancid butter and support themselves by keeping sheep, and working up wool, and are renowned for their oil-presses, and the Condrenians with the Austrian customs, and their fulling-mills for making serge. While above the Condrenians, on the top of the hill full of ravines, stands the famous Neamtzu Castle, surrounded by thickets, covered with lichen, inhabited during the summer by cattle strayed from their enclosures, and guarded by owls, and kites which have thought it a good place to build their nest in... But this has nothing to do with me, the lad from Humuleshti. I have other work to do; I want to tell the story of our village and of my childhood there, and all the rest of it.

As many Rulers and Metropolitans as have succeeded each other on the Moldavian throne since the country existed, have passed at least once through Humuleshti on their road to the monasteries. But how to describe the other people, all of them rich and superior folk, who have taken their way through our town to the Neamtzu Monastery, to the miracle-working Icon, to the madhouse, to the patronal feast of Ispas, and to the fair which is held in the marketplace then; and all who have gone to the fairs at Piatra at Pentecost, and at Fălticeni on St. Elias Day, at Secu on the feast of the Decapitation of St. John the Baptist, at Agapia-on-the-Hill at the feast of Transfiguration, at Agapia-in-the-Valley on the feast of St. Voevozi, and at Văratic on the feast of the Assumption! People, people, and yet more people! How many consecrations and dedications of new churches! How many councils and revisions of ecclesiastics and political personages! How many hearts full of longing; how many broken and erring souls have passed through our town to the monasteries! People, people, and yet more people! And during my childhood a lot of foreign soldiers, a troop of Austrian Cavalry wearing cotton uniforms, passed through Humuleshti with drawn swords towards the convent in pursuit of the beautiful Natalitza; the Austrians caused a great commotion in the convent, and made a thorough search through all of the nuns' cells, but they did not find her; the cellarer, Pârvu, from

Neamtzu town, was quite equal to hiding even a princess underground if necessary. Luckily the nuns of Văratic knew how to quiet the soldiers by gentleness, and make them sheath their sabers, telling them that whosoever draws his sword shall perish by the sword!

But why do I bother my head with kings and emperors instead of looking back at my childhood spent in Humuleshti, and into my own affairs?

It would have been more sensible to do that from the beginning; but I was bent on showing that the Humuleshtians did not live in a bear's cave, but had the advantage of seeing people of every sort and kind.

In 1852, the day when the hospital chapel in Neamtzu town was dedicated, and the royal school opened, I together with other boys belonging to the church, stood near Vodă Ghica, who was present at the ceremony surrounded by a crowd of people, and we could not stare at him enough. And he, handsome and gracious as he was, seeing us all in a row, wearing shirts with embroidery on them, and white as the fur of a pole-cat, with magnificent jackets, and close-fitting white trousers of brush wool, and shod with small sandals, with bashfulness imprinted on our faces, and the fear of God in our hearts, threw a fatherly glance towards us:

"See here, children, this school and this sacred chapel, source of all spiritual comfort and joy; take advantage of them, enlighten yourselves and praise God."

These words spoken by the royal voice made a deep impression on the hearts of the crowd assembled there, and without delay the school was filled with boys anxious to learn, among them myself, first in all the rows, and renowned for my laziness; I had become lazy without equal, for mother made up her mind to not ask anything of me, so I could concentrate on study and turn myself into a priest like Father Isaiah Duhu, our professor. He was a kind man was Father Duhu when he was in a good temper, God have mercy on him! He placed the boys in classes in a way I have never seen done till then: in the summer he bought us out of his own money bucketfuls of raspberries, and all sorts of fruits which he gave us to eat, and nearly every Saturday he piled us into a cart from the Neamtzu Monastery, and took us to the Priory to pass our examinations before the Prior Neonil, an old cripple with one foot, who advised us, in the spirit of kindness, to stick to the Book of Hours, and the Psalter. "For all other learning," said he, "is nothing but heresy which makes the heart more bitter and troubles man's mind." But it was ordained that Father Duhu should not listen to all the pious prior's advice, and he taught us a little arithmetic and grammar and geography, something of them all, according to our understanding.

Once Father Duhu came from the monastery hot with anger, and for our Rule of Three he gave us the following subject:

"If one para taken dishonestly loses one hundred

honest ones, how much will six thousand lei (my yearly salary) which Prior Neonil has wrongfully taken from me lose the Neamtzu Monastery?"

"Twenty-four million paras, honored Father, or six hundred thousand lei," answered one of us, with a bit of chalk on the blackboard.

"Let Nică Oshlobanu verify that for me," said Father Duhu.

Nică Oshlobanu as usual sprang to his feet, tall and lanky as he was, and begged to be excused as he had a headache. And then, I don't know how it happened, a great ball dropped out of his shirt, and rolled through the class, not the kind one plays with but one made of polenta, filled with cheese, round, fried on the embers, and fine to put inside one when one's hungry! The boys tried to catch it, Oshlobanu flung himself into the midst of them to seize it, and there was such a scuffle and roar of laughter through the school over the polenta; it was a lark! Even now I can see how Father Duhu clapped his hand to his forehead, saying, with a deep sigh:

"Perhaps my great and wicked sins have cast me here to teach these wild boors. You would have been a thousand times happier tending pigs on Old Cogeasca, Isaiah, than living through days like these. But you, you yokel Oshlobanu, who are a slave to your belly, and give as little trouble as you can to your brain, you'll be a priest like your father when all the buffaloes at Neamtzu Monastery have turned anchorites."

Oshlobanu was silly and simple, but don't let

anyone cross him for then he would throw dust over his head like a bull. When he went home that evening he told his father what Father Duhu had said. But trust Oshlobanu's father! Although he did not know much, and mixed up the prayers for the dead in quantities, for monks and priests, for priors and metropolitans, for their wives and for their children as fast as ever he could!

One day Father Duhu evidently had nothing to do! He took Teofan, an old monk from the hospital, and they went together to St. Lazarus' Church, below the Castle Hill. And when they entered the church he began to question Father Oshlobanu, who was officiating, as to why he did not keep the rubric.

"Rubric, you hypocrite ox? I'll rubric you," said Father Oshlobanu, setting the Mass on one side. "By a trick you took from us the great martyr Dumitru, Fountain of Holy Oil, and have given us instead of that famous saint, this Lazarus, a vacillating Jew who dies and then lives, and lives and then dies, and no one knows anything about. Is that a patron saint? And after impoverishing us by taking our land, and enclosing the church with a wall you now enclose the gateway of the hospital in the town; we are even prevented ringing the bells by these hypocritical learned men, and all on your account, and the people are scattered, not a penny do they give to the church. And one thing more, for sixty odd years I have served the priesthood, and now you come and teach me the rubric, son of a viper that you are! You wait a bit, I'll knock the nonsense out of your head!" and whrrr! He threw the large prayer book at the monks. Then seizing a heavy candlestick of brass he was after them! And Father Duhu and Teofan took to their heels, and fled, more on all fours than upright, in accordance to the rubric...

The next day Nică Oshlobanu did not come again to the school nor Father Duhu to the church of St. Lazarus, for Father Oshlobanu would have had him nailed to a cross and stored him in the granary of the church with the fragments of the icons from Neamtzu Castle that were kept there. And it seemed to me the old man was very right, for instead of the church of St. Lazarus there used to be an old wooden church whose patron was St. Dumitru, which had been built, and endowed with the estate of Voivode Vasile Lupu, like ours in Humuleshti. But the Neamtzu Monastery, very cunningly, when it built the hospital in Neamtzu town also rebuilt the church of St. Dumitru in stone, changed its patron, calling him St. Lazarus, and enclosed it within the hospital grounds by a wall, and gave the patron saint St. Dumitru to the hospital chapel, while the priests grabbed it for their estate as they did the Humuleshti property. Hence Father Oshlobanu's anger reached its height; let no monk come near his church or he would kill him! Only by the skin of his teeth did Father Duhu escape being made a martyr in the place of St. Dumitru, Fountain of Holy Oil.

A few days after this event we were told that Nică Oshlobanu had gone to study at the Catechist school at Falticeni, and it was a fact. My cousin, Ion

Mogorogea, Gâtlan, Trăsnea, and others of my acquaintance, had gone there some time previously; naturally at the expense of their fathers' pockets. So I, left without any suitable companions, and moreover Father Duhu unexpectedly giving me a beating, teased mother to persuade father to send me to the Catechist, although I was only half grown up.

Money, beehives, sheep, horses, cows, and other trifles of that kind turned into cash, had to be given by the scholars to the Catechist at the priest factory at Fălticeni, and then you must leave it to the pious Conta to turn you out little priests all of a pattern...

But for me my father gave only two bushels of wheat and two of oats to the right person, and I was accepted at Fălticeni; for the school was nothing but a means of taking money. I arrived late at night, and went to lodge with Pavel, the bootmaker in Rădăsheni Street, where were my other friends. The Catechist, who turned day into night and night into day playing faro, rarely came to the school. When we saw this we went more rarely still; I know we committed plenty of follies. Pavel was a bachelor, and his house quite spacious; benches and beds were placed all around the room, and there was one near the stove; all of them were occupied. The landlord, working day and night, sat in all his glory near the oven among his lasts, models, bench, clog, cutting-out scissors, and bevel, needles, awl, pincers, file, hammer, vice, skins, thread, pot of sulphate of iron, glue, and all the things a bootmaker needs. With us lived Bodrângă, an old fellow without a home, full of fun. For a little food and some common tobacco at 3 ozs. for a centime, he served the whole house; he cut wood, lit the fire, carried water, swept, and told us tales the whole night long, sitting with his nose in the embers, or he played on the flute, Doinas that filled one with emotion, the Corăbiasca, the Măriutza, the Horodinca, the Alivenc, the Tziitura, At the Courtyard Gate, and other tunes like that, that make you feel inclined to dance, and we did dance till the floor rocked, and the soles nearly came off our boots, heels and all. For by then I too wore boots, and owing to Mosh Bodrângă's good fairy Pavel never came to the end of the mending, and sometimes losing his head, he wore his own boots to ribbons dancing with us. Once it was Oshlobanu's turn to buy wood, and so, being very stingy, he went unwillingly to the square near our house, and found a peasant from Sasca, I think it was, or from Baia, with a cart loaded with beech logs.

"How much do you want for the cartload, friend?" said Oshlobanu, who was inclined to buy wood about as much I am now to become a priest.

"Sixty kreutzers, student."

"What are you talking about, my fine friend, for an armful of wood? Even if I carry the lot on my back to the house?"

"If you can carry it I'll give it to you for nothing."

"Really, are you joking?"

"It's not a joke, I mean it, student, let's see how you carry it, all luck to you!"

Then Oshlobanu took the logs out of the man's cart, one by one, and placed them upright, after that he undid his belt, tied the logs carefully together so as not to injure it, then raising them, he swung them with difficulty on to his back and took them into the house. A wild boy close by, upon seeing this, shouted:

'Prudent,
'Student,
'Be-he-hu!
'The devil get you!'

But the peasant, making the sign of the cross, stood open-mouthed, uttering not a word. Now I can't tell you how laden that cart was with wood, which in that place cost seven and half lei at that time, nor how big and strong were Nica Oshlobanu and about sixteen others like him, many of whom had left a wife and maybe two or three children in the recesses of the mountains, and come to Fălticeni to turn themselves into somebodies. And they studied there and no mistake: some sang even the Psalter with a great air till they were as hoarse as donkeys: others could recite on end, with their eyes shut, the seven mysteries of the Great Catechism; Gâtlan wrestled even in his sleep with the giant Goliath; the heavily mustached David from Farcasha, before one could prepare the polenta, succeeded in repeating by heart, quickly and without a mistake, all Filaret Scriban's Old Testament history, divided into periods, and the dative and accusative cases of the conjunctive pronouns out of Mărculescu's grammar:

"To me, to thee, to him, to us, to you, to them; me, thee, him, us, you, them."

Whoever made that up ought to go to the devil! Some gabbled like maniacs till exhaustion overcame them; others only murmured, reading till they almost lost their eyesight; some moved their lips as though convulsed with epilepsy; many others wandered vaguely about or remained lost in thought, realizing how they were losing their time, and knowing what cares awaited them at home. And such shaking of heads and twisting of tongues as there was among those unhappy scholars it's never been my lot to see; it was an awful joy that made one mad, God help us!

It was a great pleasure to see David, a lad from the mountains; with forked beard and fine sideburns, with hair curly and black as a crow's feathers, with a broad, serene brow, with bushy eyebrows, with great eyes as black as mulberries, and flashing like lightning with cheeks as rosy as peonies, tall of stature, broad-shouldered, slender-waisted, graceful as a birch tree, agile as a goat, and shy as a girl. God have mercy on him! He had not the change of becoming a priest; he died, poor thing, before his time, suffocated by conjunctive pronouns; may their names be forgotten for all eternity for destroying such a dear lad! More sense had Mirăutză from Grumăzeshti, during the winter months he wandered in and out of the Jews' shops asking either for sickle-cases, or fleas' bridles, or osiers from Noah's Ark, or wild strawberries for someone who happened to be going mad, or he sang to spite the Jews:

"I don't care if a beetle
Has eaten the beech-tree's leaves
But I do care if the caterpillar
Has eaten the tender green,
And not left a bough to flourish,
And give the warrior shade."

And any other nonsense that came into his head. Was he mad to lose his life for the sake of "to me, to thee, to him, to us, to you, to them, and me, thee, him, us, you, them," like David did?

I, like Mirăutză, did not tire myself to such an extent as to die from studying; for though no children would weep for me at home I was not going to give the Catechist quite such as present as that just then. For two bushels of wheat and two of oats I was not going to leave the priest of Old Fălticeni's daughter unconsoled. Besides this, when I looked in the glass I saw that of beard and mustaches there were no signs, and although I singed them, and anointed them every evening with grease, candle-fat, and burnt walnut, I worked in vain. When one belonged to such a school as that one, alas, all one needed was a beard and a purse to become a priest! Trăsnea, poor fellow, broke his heart over grammar.

Once he said to me, full of misery:

"Shtefănescu (so they called me at Fălticeni) today I shall not go to school for I don't know the lesson, and I want to learn the grammar for tomorrow, I beg of you to come with me across the plain towards Old Fălticeni; we will learn together or separately, I the grammar, and you anything you like, then you shall hear me, and we'll see if even my head can't get something into it. I don't learn very much of other things with all these new words that have come out, but this accursed grammar is turning my hair white, the devil take it! What does the church want with it? But there, if they ask for it I must get it into my head, and perhaps with you who have passed through Father Duhu's hands I may understand it..."

As there was some consolation for me in Old Fălticeni I agreed with Trăsnea, and we went together. There was a black frost that month of November, and a keen wind blew that day which was enough to freeze one's face. When we reached the plain Trăsnea threw himself down on the boundary path, and began the grammar from the beginning with the first question and answer:

Question: What is Romanian grammar?

Answer: Romanian grammar is the art which teaches us how to speak and write in the tongue correctly.

While the other edition has:

Grammar is a study which shows us how to speak and write well in a language.

This was the way of it; from the Breviary one went on to the Psalter, and after all that devil's tangle, one passed on to grammar. And what a grammar it was! Not like this crowd of grammars, some of them with "roots", others with "evolution", encumbered with "complements" which, to speak without compliments, are explained until one does not understand a word: that is to say it was compiled for children, for them to play with, as simple as they were! But what was the good! Trăsnea had not had such luck, he had no choice. He, poor soul, you see what kind of grammar he had to learn: "The art, correct, a language; a syllable we call a complete sound, simple or compound, composed of one consonant or of several consonants, and which is pronounced by prolonging the voice." While in the other edition it says: "By a syllable we mean the pronunciation of one part of a word."

"Well, well! Now clear your throat, and out with it, Trăsnea, if you can." On the third page come some more jokes.

Question: How many parts has Romanian grammar?

Answer: Romanian grammar has four parts, they are (1) Etymology, (2) Syntax, (3) Orthography, and (4) Prosody.

Question: What does each part teach us?

Answer: (1) Etymology teaches us to know the various words, that is to say, it is analytical grammar.

(2) Syntax teaches us to unite the words

according to the nature of our language; it is synthetical grammar.

(3) Orthography teaches us to write well, that is to say, according to grammatical rules.

(4) Prosody teaches us to accent the syllables, and to sound them according to the nature of the words, and the aim we have in speaking.

And then "to me, to thee, to him, to us, to you, to them." And other delightful nonsense like that. One must take into account that Trăsnea was not young, a beginner, he was stupid in a way; that the professor, who was himself surprised at having become a professor, said: "Take from here to there" as it seems to me they do in some places to this day; but perhaps the trouble was neither the grammar, nor the professor, nor Trăsnea, but just the chances which have made men what they are, sometimes steel knives, sometimes tin. Then do you think Trăsnea would read the question and answer in their order, clear and plain so that one could understand something?

Not at all, credulous ones, it was like this: "What is Romanian grammar, it is... it is... is...the show, no not show, the art... the art... which... which... which... teaches us, teaches... teaches... which teaches us to speak... eak... eak, which teaches us... it is, is, is, is the show, damn it! Not the show, the art, the art which teaches us... it is..." And so on, muttering rapidly, stammering, and without a scrap of reflection; as far as "write in the tongue correctly" he rarely got, poor fellow! And when he had muddled his head altogether he called to me to hear him, he knew it. I took the book out of his hand, and asked him: "What is grammar, Trăsnea?" And he, closing his eyes, replied, quickly, and muttering like a beggar in the road asking for alms; "What is Romanian grammar, it is, it is, is..." and all the rest of it as usual, murdering the words, and pronouncing them so that they made no sense, and one nearly cried with pity.

"That isn't it, Trăsnea."

"Why not?"

"Don't say Romanian, and only give the answer; what have you to do with the question?"

And he made an effort for a second to answer properly, but in vain; he got more muddled, and began to sigh enough to split his head.

"Leave me for a while," he said sadly, "and when I call to you come again to hear me, and if I don't know it then, may the devil take me! Well, we'll say I know 'grammar' so we can leave that on one side; 'the art' same thing, 'correct' ditto. So then it's 'Romanian is... that... which teaches us to speak, and write well in the tongue.' They seem to be Romanian words, by Jove! Only there's something wrong here! 'To speak and write in the tongue', that's a mad thing! How can one 'write in the tongue?' With a tongue perhaps, how do I know? Maybe that we scrawl, and then in talking, poor thing, we speak quite roughly and clumsily, not Romanian but dialect... Lord! Lord! How learned they must be who make the grammar! And yet I see in the grammar that table is table, and house is house, and ox is ox just as I learned it from my mother. Perhaps all the other monstrous things, 'Articulation, art, correct, pronunciation, analysis, synthesis, prosody, orthography, syntax, etymology, concrete, abstract, conjunctive, to me, to thee, to him, to us, to you, to them, me, thee, him, us, you, them,' are also Romanian... but we, simpletons, have trouble with them! Luckily we don't have to sing them, for that would be worse than ever for our dull heads! Better dead than a peasant! Go off, Shtefănescu, and let me learn..."

I left him, and played a trick on him by going off to the priest's daughter; I found her alone and amused myself peacefully with her till the evening, for mother she had none, and her father, as priest, was visiting the sick. I returned to the plain with a little chain from round the girl's neck, a scarf prettily embroidered with silk flowers, and my shirt full of apples. And when I got back there was that fool of a Trăsnea asleep on the boundary path with the grammar under his nose, and almost numb with cold. "Poor thing, poor thing! It would have been better for your mother to make you a lamb, and let the wolves eat you," said I to myself.

"Hi, Trăsnea! Get up! Do you know the lesson?"

He sprang to his feet. I listened to him.... he had made nothing of it.

"Let's go home, Trăsnea, I'm mad with hunger, and bored to death on this plain."

"Yes, so am I. The devil take the grammar! I've

had enough of it! Besides I'm not well!"

"A kind of laziness mixed with weakness, Trăsnea, isn't that it?"

"You've guessed it; a kind of faintness and tightening of the heart, or something like that."

"Grammatical shivers, perchance," said I.

"How do I know, perhaps so," said Trăsnea. "The devil take it! As one puts one's hand on the book sleep overtakes one. Such trifles really are not fit for the Church. The hymnal is where it's at. As father used to say: 'The song fills the bag, the hymn fills the barn, my boy!' Why do we go about plaguing ourselves with grammar, Shtefănescu? Let's go."

We returned to our lodgings at sunset, ate what we could, and then begged Mosh Bodrângă to play to us; a crowd of students joined us as if it were their own fold, and we got excited dancing, for at that age we did not feel the night passing. And thus I was saved from being bored, and Trăsnea from babbling in his sleep, "what is Romanian grammar, is... is," and so on. And the gaiety never flagged; it only grew more intense, and began all over again. Mosh Bodrângă had scarcely taken his flute from his lips when suddenly we saw Priest Buligă, also called Corncob, from Buciumeni Street, quite drunk since early morning, God deal lightly with him! And while he was blessing us, according to his custom, with both hands like a bishop, he made allusion to the daughter of the priest of Old Fălticeni, either that she was a good girl, or would make a good priest's wife, or that she was suited to me, or that her father would tie her to my neck, and suchlike, innuendoes, inventions of his, Priest Buligă the Sneerer's, until Gâtlan began to cajole him, saying:

"Come, come, honored Father, your reverence must not continue to make such aspersions, and on the eve of the fast too. Anyhow let Mosh Bodrângă play to us a little while, that we may make merry for the Father will be so good as to excuse us."

And in truth Mosh Bodrângă began to play again, and the lads to dance. And Priest Buligă, although he was old, when he saw we meant it, tucked the shirt of his cassock into his belt, saying:

"For my part I wish God may give you joy and all good luck, my sons, that you may live happily."

His hat slipped to one side as he joined in the whirl of the dance while his plaits swayed. And we shouted again and again till we nearly knocked the breath out of the priest. And thus we tired him out until he had had enough of us. But as the proverb puts it: "If you join the game you must play." But in time the poor priest saw he had joined a crowd of lunatics, and he began to resort to subterfuge:

"I am expected at the confessional, my friends, and must go whether I will or no, for that is our work."

Then Pavel, our host, placed a plate of biscuits, and a carafe of wine before Father Buligă, saying:

"I beg of you, reverend Father, to accept from our table a little food, and a glass or two of wine, and then to go on your way as you say you are in great haste."

His reverence needed no persuasion, he crossed his hands as was his custom, cleared his voice, and said humbly:

"Bless, oh, Lord, the meat and drink of thy humble servant, Amen."

After that he raised a glass, saying:

"I drink to you, lads, as to a forest of green trees."

He drank off a glass, then two or three others, and after that a few more. Then he blessed us again with both hands saying:

"Now, my boys, begin to calm yourselves."

Then he left us in peace, and went his way. While we quoted the saying:

"Don't believe the doctor,
Don't believe the priest.
Take what comes along,
And amuse yourselves well."

Rather late at night we trooped off, Mosh Bodrângă and all, and entered a reputable inn belonging to the daughter of the Vornic of Rădăsheni, where many people gathered more for love of the landlady than for desire for wine; she was pretty, the fascinating little thing! She had lately married an old widower, and a noodle. When the landlady saw us she instantly jumped in front of us, and led us aside into a large room with blinds to the windows, and boards on the floor, where we were all to ourselves while our landlady entertained us as in her own house.

In one corner of the room there were some bushels of haricot beans, in another hemp seed; in the third a heap of apples and Rădăsheni pears which keep till after Easter; in the fourth peas and beans divided by a wide board, while close by were some Turkish melons; in an open barrel were pears as dry and sweet as figs; yonder was a pile of trusses of hemp and flax; from a beam hung brakes for the hemp; and skeins of wool dyed all colors for making plain and patterned carpets; besides there were tow, flock, and others things spread anyhow on the boards, and in the corners, as was usual to find in the house of a well-to-do citizen of that day. When we arrived at this prosperous house the landlady quickly let down the blinds, lit a light, and before one could clap one's hands, had provided us with a large earthenware vessel full of Odobeshti wine; and as it was poured out into the glasses drops of wine spirted up several inches, it was so strong. Gâtlan, the rogue, took a glass and held it out to the landlady, saying:

"Please, my dear, you must do honor to it first. We shall see, you may have put something into it."

The pretty landlady, taking the glass, drank to our health with laughing eyes, and after sipping it, begged us to excuse her for there were other customers, and her husband must not be left single-handed. But we barred her passage, and insisted upon her drinking with each one of us. And she might have stayed some while with us if we had not driven her away by trying to thank her with a hearty kiss or so!

"Such is youth, the devil take it," said Mosh Bodrângă, perched on a heap of flock and nibbling some dried pears, "you're right, my lads, now's your time!"

"It's as you say, old man," replied the landlady, coming in at the door with a tray of steaming dishes, among them a roast chicken, and putting them on the table in front of us; and really it was a charity she did for we were hungry as wolves.

When we had finished drinking the first bowl, she brought us another one for which we all thanked her with kisses until she grew angry, and ran away from us. At last she came back, and ran away again, perhaps that's how wine is sold when it is sold... But how can you tell? Maybe the landlady was not sorry to be among us as she came thus often to see us. Finally, the hideous Trăsnea embraced her without thinking what he was doing. That's what most stupidity comes from. The pretty landlady was really furious. But what could we do? The proverb says: "You have to cool down in the shirt you get hot in." There is no other way of putting it. After a time Mosh Bodrângă took heart, and began to play on his flute a Corăbiasca of the most inspiriting kind. And then didn't we get carried away by the dance! We became so excited that we forgot about the house; we went across the haricots, and through the peas and beans, and the hemp seed turned into oil flowing beneath our soles. A little after midnight, seeing that Mosh Bodrângă had deserted us, we too began,

one by one, to wander homewards; I with my shirt
loaded with dried pears, and a huge melon given me
by the landlady, for as she was beautiful so was she
generous... But when we reached our lodgings, what
do I see? Every one of my companions had purloined
something, one some Calville apples; another some
Rădăsheni pears: Mosh Bodrângă had gone off with
a pile of tow for lighting the fire, and Trăsnea with
some hemp seed. While as for Oshlobanu, whose
boots were made of one whole cowhide each, he was
the last of us all to come in, and we saw him put his
head on his bed, and his feet on the beam, shod and
dressed as he was, and then, have your eyes ever
seen the like? I am not lying, more than a bushel of
haricot beans ran out of the tops of his boots which
he usually wore tucked down, but which he had
pulled up now for this purpose... Only my cousin, Ion
Mogorogea, son of a respected citizen, took not a jot.
While Zaharia Gâtlan contented himself with a kiss
from the pretty landlady. Very comforting for a
strange lad on the eve of a fast! But now I realize
that Gâtlan, called Zaharia Simionescu at school,
was the wisest of us all; because he benefited by
what we brought while we, of his happiness... not at
all. Well, well, everything good and pleasant in their
time; after that we had to apply ourselves to our
books for soon the Christmas vacation would be
here, and we were spending our parents' goods in
vain; one can do nothing without expense, and one
does not pick up money by the roadside. One with
another we had altogether at the beginning of

Advent about four or five crocks of oil, three or four sacks of maize-flour, a few pounds of salt fish, dried pears, haricot beans, peas, beans, salt and wood for each week: we all sat round the table, giving the viands in turn, each one providing from his store for one day. But Oshlobanu, who ate enough for seventeen, made us think a bit. There was no question but that his father, Priest Necula, had plenty to send him, but "a bird in the hand is worth two in the bush."

There are many things to do and no need to say much if one has someone to confide in. I consulted one day with Gâtlan as to what was to be done to rid ourselves of some of the gluttons; for our company did not seem to us to be quite fair. And we devised a plan that could not be improved upon. At night, when they were all sleeping, we would put a plaster on the sole of whoever we selected, especially if they were sound asleep when Mosh Bodrângă began to relate his tales. When we had prepared everything we were on the watch for when the others went out of the house, and then we made up the plasters which we had by us for some time. A few sheets of paper stuck together with candle-fat melted by the fire, put gently against the sole of a chap who is fast asleep, and set alight with a match, greater sport there cannot be... And as they were all very angry with Oshlobanu it was upon him we played the trick first. And when the heat touched him he sprang out of his sleep roaring like a bull, and nowhere in the house could he find relief. But not being able to discover the culprit, or capable of fighting us all, he had to bow to facts, and curses poured upon us like fire from his lips. But we, in spite of his curses, continued to apply a plaster every night, and when the soles of his feet were just one sore he was forced to take himself to Humuleshti, sick of the priesthood, and leaving all his provisions in our hands. Soon after this Gâtlan wrote to Oshlobanu:

"DEAR OSHLOBANU,

I salute the destitute, deprived of his all. If you have nothing to eat there, we beg of you to fast with the rest of us.

Your well-wisher,

ZAHARIA,

Chief Captain of the Plasterers."

After a few days we put an end to a taste for the priesthood in one who had but recently come to us; Nică Constantin Cosma, from Humuleshti, also with blistered feet, followed in Oshlobanu's wake. And all the better; they were only spending time in vain. But Trăsnea being more obstinate, and more patient, bore it as long as he could, only when he saw we were going on with it with him he removed to another lodging taking with him a part of the provisions. And by this arrangement only three of us stayed on with Pavel, the cobbler; I, Gâtlan, my cousin Ion, nicknamed the Grumbler, and Mosh Bodrângă besides. My cousin, who looked with pity upon the others, adopted the habit, every night when he went to bed, of sewing up the sleeves of his fur-lined pelisse, and wrapping up his legs in them so that he slept without fear.

As the proverb says: "Forewarned is forearmed."

Towards Christmas, Pavel made my cousin Ion, with whom he was close friends, a pair of Russian leather boots. And they were worth money, those boots, for he used good leather, and thick soles, and they were well sewn. Only Pavel forgot to make them squeak... and by that he cut Mogorogea to the heart. Luckily it was a frosty winter, and the snow helped with the squeaking.

For the holidays we went home, and then came what the gypsies call "a glutton's Christmas"; cutlets of smoked pork, rolls and galantine; sausage of garlic and fine lard, made at home, cut off and fried with hot polenta, slips down the throat like butter. The peasant makes other kinds of savory dishes too when he has the wherewithal to make them. And thank God our parents had the means, for poverty never knocked at their door as far as I know. But I must not forget my story; we passed happy holidays with our parents at Humuleshti, and after the Feast of the Epiphany we returned again to Fălticeni, to Pavel our landlord. To the school we also returned sometimes for appearance sake. But to speak plainly we got nothing out of it because the alphabet anyone can learn at home if he wants to. But he who does not is a lucky fellow. And I was one among those happy fellows; to tell the truth, what does one want with learning? Even I say that Mosh Bodrângă had something to teach us; his flute would make you dance in spite of yourself, and his tales gave you no time for sleep. Besides that, we had other ways of passing the time if we liked; we played cards, or at other times at night we started spinning yarns till daybreak. On holidays we went together through the villages where we knew there was dancing. In Rădăsheni, a large, pleasant, and well-to-do place we joined in three different dances on one day: one for bachelors of thirty who were joined by very young girls; another for very young men who were joined by spinsters of twenty-five, while the third was for young men of nineteen or twenty, and anyone who pleased might join. The young men hardly moved in the dance, and the circle turned very slowly. The girls did not wait to be asked as they do in other places, but each one, holding out a hand to two boys whom she chose, said "how do you do," and joined in the dance. My cousin, peacocking about in his new boots, only danced next to the Vornic's daughter, sister to the landlady of Fălticeni. And Gâtlan who was dancing next me, whispered to me:

"You'll see what I'll do to Mogorogea, he won't enjoy today, I'm blessed if he does!"

"You be quiet," said I, "you're talking without rhyme or reason, you'll make the fellow angry, and he'll go home too."

"And if he does? What a loss! The proverb says: 'If the old dame descends from the carriage she scarcely makes it lighter for the mares!' " And we danced on.

In the evening we went back to our lodging, and

Mogorogea, a careful lad, cleaned his boots thoroughly, and put them to dry on the stove, at one side, as he always did. The third day after this my cousin's boots split all over. And he, in the highest degree incensed, insisted to Pavel that he should make him a pair in their place, or return him the money at once.

"You gave me too dry skins, bungler," said Mogorogea, furiously. "What kind of a friend to me are you? Come, choose one of the two, otherwise I'll put you to shame, and throw the boots at your head. Do you hear me?"

"Just listen, Student Mogorogea; don't be violent, and use words which don't become you. Who do you call a bungler? After you have worn the boots all this time, prowling about all day, and scratching them at the dance, and going through all sorts of ravines and precipices, now you want me to give you the money back, or make you new ones? But you must be mad! Isn't it enough for you that you have worn me out putting them on the last, stretching them, and greasing them at the oven under my nose every morning? And how many times have you put plasters on my feet and I, like a good fellow, never said a word and put up with you? I am sorry you are so insolent. And it's certain I'll not work for you if you talk like that."

"What do you say, you bungler," said my cousin, "you are grumbling at me? When I have worn your boots only, miserable man? Yet you are insolent. Now I'll maim you with something so that you cannot earn any more all your life."

"Before you maim me," said Pavel, "I'll mince you up with my clog, do you understand?"

When we saw they were on the point of fighting each other we put ourselves between them, and with great difficulty reconciled them. Ion gave Pavel another coin while Pavel put new tops to the boots... and peace was made.

They joked about this quarrel, but Mogorogea never forgot the affront Pavel had put upon him. In Holy Week, Mosh Vasile, coming to Fălticeni, among other provisions, brought his son three sucking pigs already prepared.

"I'm glad you have arrived all right, Father," said Ion, kissing his hand. "You find us well."

"I'm glad to find you well, boys," replied Mosh Vasile.

Then he said:

"I arrived in the dark at Suceava, and nearly did not arrive at all." Then he questioned us minutely: "And what does the Mecet say about you becoming a priest? Is he ready to let you go right away? For to tell you frankly I am sick of so much trouble and expense."

"One doesn't say Mecet but Catihet, father," replied Ion, blushing.

"Na, na, na, my fine gentleman, do you think I care about that? The proverb says: 'It's six of one and half a dozen of the other.' Mecet, Berechet, Pleshcan, whatever they are called, Ion, I know they fleece us well." said Mosh Vasile. "One must be on one's guard with a priest! You better pray with all your heart to the blessed Hierarch Nicholas of Humuleshti that he may help you to find yourself priest one day. And then... you will have escaped from all worries; you won't have to pay taxes or give free labor; at the table you will sit in the seat of honor, and eat of all the hot dishes, and roast chicken. They'll even pay you teeth money!... The proverb says: 'A priest needs a horse's hoof, a wolf's jaw, a thick skin, and a mare's belly, and nothing else!' It would be well, God forgive me, if the sons of the Church were different!... But you must have heard that a priest's hand takes, but never gives; he fleeces both the living and the dead. You see Mecet lives well... without working as we do... only... well... one must give a little present! Ion, I have got my eye on a post for you," said Mosh Vasile, as he went away. "Don't be downhearted, lay your hand at your certificate as soon as you can, and come home, for Ioana Grigorash Roshu of our town is eagerly waiting to make you a priest's wife. Good-bye, Student Zaharia, and nephew, I must be off."

"A good journey, Mosh Vasile," we said, going part of the way with him. "Please tell our parents that we are well and miss them."

After Mosh Vasile had gone I said ingratiatingly to Ion:

"Cousin, let's roast one of those pigs this evening for I am dying for some." Mogorogea, obstinate and stingy as he was, began to shout at me:

"Listen, I'm not Nică Oshlobanu for you to treat

as you please... Whatever you give me to eat that will I give you to eat. I won't give you a scrap of pig even if you burst yourself."

"Unless him who speaks so bursts," replied Gâtlan.

"Amen," I mumbled half-heartedly.

"And I say amen too," said Pavel, from near the stove.

"Amen or not amen, the pig is off as far as you're concerned," said Mogorogea, passionately. "Do you understand? Don't be always running after food; you can go without for you'll get nothing."

"Let him be, may he choke on them in the next world!" said Zaharia.

And we started, good Lord, to learn. But we used to say "We don't like to learn any better than a dog likes to lick salt." A fierce fire was burning in the stove; it overpowered us, and made us drowsy although there was a frost outside. Mosh Bodrângă loitered, I know not where, that evening, and Pavel not having his usual work went to bed early. Mogorogea full of hope in his father's post went to sleep before Pavel, with his feet in the sleeves of his pelisse as usual, and snored loudly. The proverb says: "Leave me alone and I'll leave you alone." Later we too put out the light, and went to bed, but we could not sleep for thinking of the pig.

"You, Zaharia, surely you've a plaster or so somewhere," said I, softly.

"No, friend," replied Zaharia, still more softly. "Lord it would be fun to clap one on to Mogorogea.

But never mind about a plaster, don't mind anything, take my little knife, and carefully cut the seam of Mogorogea's sleeve to the right of one of his soles, and give him a good burning with some of the matches which burn dully, and then we'll see what use his pigs are to him... Only don't be long..."

"Give me the knife here," said I, "but through all this adventure I trust to you not to make a fool of me, or let him beat me."

"Of course there's no question of that," said Zaharia, "just burn him and don't worry."

Then I took my courage between my teeth, and did exactly what Gâtlan had said; I cut the seam carefully, and held a bundle of lighted matches to my cousin's heel where the skin was the thickest until the flame reached him. And when he groaned once loudly I, whirr! Matches in hand, a spring, and I was the other side of Zaharia, and we began to snore as if we had been asleep for who knows how long... while Ion, encumbered by his feet being in the sleeves of his pelisse, fell flat on the floor, and writhing like a serpent, cursed with any oath that rose to his lips:

"Alas! May God punish you, wretched creatures that you are! No one can rest in this house owing to your wickedness. Which one has played me this trick? Zaharia and Nică I can hear snoring, besides I don't think they would dare. Only that brigand Pavel can have done this to me... The insect would sting just when sleep was sweetest. And now the beast pretends to sleep. I'll teach him not to play tricks on a fellow again!"

And with the tongs he quickly took a live coal from the hearth, and carried it across to Pavel who was by the stove. And as the poor man was sleeping face upwards Mogorogea put the coal on his bare chest, saying:

"Na! Take your fill of the joke you played on me, bungler!"

Then was heard a terrifying roar, and simultaneously with the roar, Pavel struck the stove with his feet, and turned it over on to the floor. In this confusion he met Ion face to face, and a terrible battle began between the two; you may stay and watch it if you have the heart to...

"You know, Zaharia, if a man dies in the house we'll have to give evidence," said I, trembling like a leaf, with fear.

"Ho, you two, what's the matter with you," said Zaharia, hopping like a vulture between them. "Do you call this a house for decent men?"

I flung myself out of the door crying, and began to yell as loud as I could, shouting to the neighbors. People ran up from all sides, confused, thinking there was a fire, or that the soldiers were cutting us down, which God forbid! For there was an Austrian Army in Fălticeni at that time. After that idea was exploded the people left us as they found us, and dispersed, jeering at us. You should have seen the damage and mess there was in the house, broken windows, a stove upset, tufts of hair pulled out of their heads, blood on the floor, Pavel with a burnt chest, and Ion sitting exhausted on one side with a roasted heel; I with Zaharia, on the other side, marveling at what had happened... while the innocent pigs that had been hanging up in the cool corridor were nowhere to be found! After a time Zaharia, anxious to break the silence, said:

"Now, Ion, sing to them 'Those without stain, Hallelujah,' and don't go on longing after them, evidently it was so ordained for them, the little mites!"

"Now you keep your mouth shut," replied Ion, much depressed; "you've talked so much about it that you've made it work out the way you wanted."

During these words Mosh Bodrângă arrived a little drunk, and began to cross himself in the doorway.

"Well, old man," said I, "are you pleased with the state you find us in?"

Pavel, who up to then had sat as one dumb, gazing with disgust at the room, said:

"Listen, students, to finish with this quarrelling you decamp from here, and leave me in peace."

We, happy to have escaped so lightly, took all we had, and moved to a blacksmith's across the road together with Mosh Bodrângă, our comforter. During the Lent Fast a rumor spread among the students of the disestablishment of the Catechists, and the transference of the young ones among us to Socola.

"It's a good job that I've done with it," said Trăsnea. "I tell you there's nothing in it. The proverb says: 'We stake our all to learn.' Why the devil should I worry my head with grammar? I know this,

I'd rather stay safely at home, and what with the money which has been spent here, and spent there, my father will have some worry."

"And we," said the married students, sighing, "we are quite ruined; we know that sheep and beehives and oxen have all gone into the wolf's jaw. Long live the Father Catechist!"

"Be quiet, friends," replied Zaharia, " 'money is the devil's eye' as the proverb runs. Why do you abuse the worthy Catechist? Is he the only one? And then, you fellows, I don't really know how one could please you. As the saying has it: 'Go in a chariot! No! Go in a carriage! No! Go in a cart! No! Go on foot! No!' You better go back to your like as water flows back to the river bed. I'm very glad this has happened. To Socola we must go if we want to come out on top. There are the most learned professors in the world there according to what I hear."

"To Socola," cried the youngest of the scholars.

"Go to the devil if you like, go, and soar round the larks," said the old ones.

As Easter drew near we separated from one another, but whoever wished was allowed to go to Socola in the coming autumn of the year 1855.

# CHAPTER IV

AS HARD as it is to draw a bear from his den, to settle a mountaineer on the plains, to take an infant from its mother's breast, just so hard was it for me to leave Humuleshti in the autumn of the year 1855, when it was time to go to Socola according to mother's decision. And why did I not want to leave Humuleshti on any account, when mother told me so often that it was for my good? Well, this was why I did not want to; I was a young man by now, and Jassy which I had never seen was not near Neamtzu like Fălticeni; from there in late autumn, and especially during the winter carnivals, when the nights are long, I could from time to time, slipping away directly after the Angelus, one night in the month, hasten over with my companions to a party at Humuleshti; we knew we must go like race-horses; but after we had danced as hard as we could, we stole a kiss from some of the pretty girls, and quitting the village towards dawn... somewhere about midday found ourselves again at Fălticeni; passing barefoot across the ford to the right of Baia, both going and coming, with the Moldova River frozen to its banks, was enough to freeze the marrow in one's bones! But our hearts were high, and what we planned we carried to success.

From Neamtzu to Fălticeni, and from Fălticeni to Neamtzu was but a hand's breadth for us. But now it would be a different story; a short journey of two posting-stages from Fălticeni to Neamtzu was not to be compared with a distance of six posting-stages, long and tiring, from Jassy to Neamtzu. It was no joke going from Neamtzu to Jassy or from Jassy to Neamtzu; that's the long and the short of it. Much better stay where you are, Ion, thought I with my simple mind, sooner than weep unconsoled and pine away with longing for someone dear to your eyes! But the proverb says: "The bear does not play with a good grace." Whether I would or not I had to do what mother wanted, to go unwillingly, and leave what was dear to me.

Dear to me was our village with the Ozana, a lovely stream as clear as crystal which had mirrored for so many centuries the mournful castle of Neamtzu. Dear to me were my father and mother, my brothers and sisters, and the boys of the village, companions of my childhood, with whom in the frosty winter days I disported myself upon the ice, and on the slide; while in the summer on holidays, singing and shouting, we wandered through the forests and shady meadows, along the shores of the lake, across the ploughed fields, the flowering plain, and over the stately hills from behind which rose the rays of dawn to laugh at me so full of the gaiety of youth! Dear to me too were the working meetings, the parties, the dances, and all the other amusements of the village in which I took part with the greatest enthusiasm. You must be made of stone if you could have helped your heart leaping with joy when you heard at times, in the silence of the night, Mihai, the flutist from Humuleshti, wandering through the village with a group of lads behind him, singing:

"Among the green leaves of the chicory
Tonight in the cool air,
A nightingale sang
With the voice of a maiden;
It sang so suavely,
The leaves fluttered from the tree,
And it sang so mournfully,
For our parting was near;
And it sighed and trilled,
Almost it broke one's heart."

And how many other songs did not Mihai sing and play on his violin; and many other pleasures full of gaiety did we have: it seemed the year was one holiday! An old woman said: "May God make the whole year a holiday with only one day for work, and may even that be a day of feast and weddings." Boy, leave the village with all its attractions, and pass on to a strange place far away if your wretched heart permits. I made every effort at first to make my mother understand that I should be ill with longing for her... and die among strangers, that my cousin Ion Mogorogea, Gheorghe Trăsnea, Nică Oshlobanu, and others had ceased to study, and moreover were living in their parents' houses. But it was labor lost, mother had other ideas; she got me ready with all necessary care, saying to me at one moment, with asperity:

"Ion, don't make me humiliate you, and do stop this discussion... You've to go where I tell you. And Zaharia Gâtlan goes with you. Mosh Luca, our neighbor, will drive you in a carriage with a pair of horses like dragons. It would be as well of you to run off now to him to see if he is ready for the road. For tomorrow, early, please God, you will start."

"I'm not going, mother, I'm not going to Socola even if you kill me," said I, crying ten rows of tears. "Let the people live without priests."

"It's no use you still making a fuss, Ion," replied my mother, impatiently, "that's no use with me...I think you know my way... Now don't treat me to this, or I'll take the maize-stick from its niche, and coax you with that, for all you're so big!"

Then, she called to father, and said authoritatively:

"Tell the boy, man, what he ought to do, that he may pluck up courage, and set out on his way."

"There's nothing more to be said about this," said father, gloomily. "He has to do what we think, and not what he wishes; he's not old enough to judge. If that were my only care, wife, what would it matter? But I'm wrestling with the thought of how I shall bear the expense, for money is not to be gathered at the foot of the trees like dead wood. And there are six here besides himself, and if he remains here he won't require anything, will he? But as he's the eldest he must have a chance; we must let him try his wings for man cannot tell what the days may bring. And maybe one day he will be a support to the others."

When I saw there was no way of opposing my parents I began to think about starting, saying to myself bitterly:

"What a misfortune for me! The priests in our village have never trotted through Socola, the saints have pity on them. They don't have to tighten their belts, fat old things that they are! And then the monks; a band of lazy good-for-nothings from all over the place, nesting in the monasteries, what don't they get to! And I have been through a series of schools, in Humuleshti, at Broshteni, in the recesses of the mountains, in Neamtzu, at Fălticeni, and now at Socola to prepare the way for my becoming a simple priest with a wife and children; that was asking a lot of me!"

Now I would tell mother that I would turn monk in Neamtzu, or at Secu. And with all the books I know and with all the books I don't know I could in a few years arrive at being the head of a religious hostel, and pick up a nice pot of money like Father Chirilash of Vânători Neamtzu. And then... pose as a pious Hilary, a flask of brandy at one's hip and as much soft fishes' roes as possible with other dainties in the pocket of one's tunic, pistols in the belt under one's frock, one's hat on one side, and the sword of the Holy Spirit in one's hand, and one's plaits streaming in the breeze, take one's way over the "Wicked Foot" towards the "Devil's Path" between Secu and Agapia-on-the-Hill where every summer an angel voice can be heard singing;

"Here in the bed of the stream
Is standing the ewe of God."

While a rough voice responds:

"I come springing from Durau,
And I am the ram of God."

For without wishing to do so, I learnt, poor sinner, some monkish mysteries while wandering in the summer with some boys in search of mushrooms in those parts, and that is where I got my leaning towards the monkhood... You know man is attracted by piety.

Finally, I must not forget to say how all the last night before leaving, till dawn broke, I revolved in my mind every sort and kind of way in which I could influence my mother to let me go to the monastery, but just when I had decided to tell mother this, behold the sunrise announcing a glorious day, and Mosh Luca, who was married for the second time to a young wife who was careful to wake him up punctually, and prepare him for the journey... could be heard shouting outside: "Are you ready? Let's start. I'm waiting for you with horses ready harnessed." Then mother took me off to the starting-place so hurriedly that I could not tell her about the monkhood.

Well, to make a long story short, we assembled with Zaharia's relations and mine, in Mosh Luca's yard, we kissed our parents' hands, and said goodbye with our eyes swimming with tears, and after we had mounted the carriage, miserable and sobbing, Mosh Luca our driver whipped up the horses, saying to his wife, who shut the door after us; "Olimbiadă, look out for that hole." For some pigs had broken the fence at one place, and were pushing through the maize in the garden.

It was early morning on the Feast of the Decapitation of St. John the Baptist when we left Humuleshti, and girls and boys charmingly dressed for the holiday were strolling through the village on all sides with pleasure imprinted on their faces. Only Zaharia and I, groaning in Mosh Luca's carriage, were on the way to uncalled for exile. For I can give it no better name.

"Please drive faster, Mosh Luca," said I, "so that the village cannot stare at us as though we were bears."

But Mosh Luca drove as he thought best for his screws were quite tired out, and as weak and thin as any starving cat, and not like dragons as declared my mother, who had not known how to get me out of the house fast enough.

"Whoever thought of dispersing the catechists just in our time ought to be damned," said Zaharia Gâtlan, full of oppression, after we got on the road beyond our village. "When you are enjoying your youth you have to study as if a man had ten lives. We wander from school to school, more often than not quite uselessly, and one day we wake to find ourselves prematurely old, pale and sickly, and only fit to be priests who have been educated at Socola. What do you say, Mosh Luca, about this?"

"What do I say, Student Zaharia, what do I know about your schools? I have to take you to the place agreed upon, and from here to there one must use one's head on your behalf. Go on, my beauties, that we may get home all the sooner."

When we heard Mosh Luca thinking of home so fondly, and when we saw we were leaving villages and other pretty spots behind us, and that other, unknown ones, were taking shape before us, our despair reached its height. At each fountain, stream, ravine, forest, and other beloved placed which we left behind we heaved a deep sigh. We had a mind to turn back even then if we had not been in Mosh Luca's charge, and we should have been ashamed of ourselves before him, and before our parents.

After a short halt at Timisheshti Bridge across the Moldova River, we proceeded forwards towards Motzca, and slowly, slowly, climbed up through the Pashcani Forest. From the top of the Forest, we poor outcasts threw once more an agonized glance at the Neamtzu mountains; mighty mountains with crests hidden in the clouds, where springs rise, and whence streams come rushing down, whispering mysteriously in their restless passage, perhaps carrying with them many human griefs and ills to drown them in the great Danube.

"Well, well, Zaharia," said I, as we descended the valley towards Pashcani, "from henceforth we lose sight of the mountains, and our banishment is an accomplished fact for who knows how long!"

"As God Almighty has ordained," said Zaharia, in a voice that was almost inaudible. We remained lost in thought all the way to Blăgeshti on the other side of the Sireth where we were to lodge for the night. But what an awful lodging! We were on a wheelwright's verandah, and there was little left of us. From twilight till after midnight we were in a cloud of smoke from the manure heap as if we were in quarantine, and none the less the mosquitoes devoured us all right.

"Such is life on the plains," said Mosh Luca, writhing and twisting himself as if on hot coals on account of the mosquitoes. "After one crosses the Sireth the water is bad, and the woods scarce, while during the summer one is overcome with heat, and the mosquitoes bite one ferociously. I would not live in the plains, God forbid! It's all right with us. The waters are sweet, clear as crystal and cold as ice; there are enough forests; during the summer there is shade, and coolness everywhere; and the people are healthy and strong, good and lively, but it's not like that in the plains; they are pale and wrinkled as if they had eaten nothing but mushrooms all their lives."

"You know one thing, Mosh Luca," said Zaharia, after a time; "the Pleiades are in the east, and the Plough is too and the morning star will soon be up, let us go on our way."

"You say well, Student Zaharia, as though a saint had spoken through your lips. And on this verandah one can only turn and twist, it is much better to get out of it. May God Almighty keep us from accidents!"

And so, with a farewell to the landlord, who with his family was sleeping on another verandah, we departed. And when we got on to the high road we found our idea had been a good one for we fell in with men with carts, full of wooden tiles, and we joined them for fear of the wandering gypsies from Ruginoasa, and we went on and on and on and on, till daybreak founds us at Târgu-Frumos where we cut up some watermelons which satisfied immediately both hunger and thirst. After the horses had rested we proceeded to the Iloa bridge, and from there on towards Jassy, but much more often on foot than in the carriage, for Mosh Luca's dragons were nearly dead, and our peasants, wags that they are, whoever met us, laughed at us in passing, until we were ashamed of Mosh Luca's shame. And particularly at sunset, just when we entered Jassy by the Păcurari Gate, a son of a devil laughed at us properly, saying:

"Old man, take care you hold in your steeds in case they bolt, for Jassy at large, and God forbid you should do any harm."

One thing you can rely upon Mosh Luca for, he'll pour out curses and insults on that fellow... "But did you ever hear such a thing! If he only knew what knaves and torments I've come from this night he would have kept his mouth shut, and would not have joked about my horses. Besides, I'm not in Jassy for the first time to need advice from the likes of him as to what I ought to do. His mother was four-tenths of a good-for-nothing. If he'd only stayed a minute I'd have taught him not to make fun of travelers."

When we saw that everybody was laughing at us, and Mosh Luca thoroughly upset, as we were in the carriage, we covered ourselves up entirely with the rug, and I said diffidently:

"Mosh Luca, if henceforth anyone should ask you why the horses are going so slowly, tell them you are carrying some blocks of salt from Ocna, they'll all believe you."

"Eh! What's that? If I'd known you were going to treat me so!" said Mosh Luca, walking by the side of his horses, full of woe. "Don't you do it, or I'll give you some blows with a stick through that rug that will cure the devil out of you!..."

When we heard what was in store for us we cuddled up against each other, joking in a low voice, but we said not a word. At last, after many taunts received by Mosh Luca from one and another, for the world is unkind, and going at a foot's pace, step by step, at haphazard through the by-streets of Jassy, we arrived rather late at night in the Socola grounds, and drew up the carriage under a big poplar where we found a crowd of students assembled from all the Catechists in the province of Moldavia: some were very young, while most of the others had bears as long as brushes; they were sitting on the grass with their parents and priests and advisors, and were confessing their sins to each other...

~ The End ~